CONDITIONING FOR WRESTLING

CONDITIONING FOR WRESTLING

Pre-season

Regular Season

and

Off-season

By

ROBERT R. SPACKMAN JR., M.S., R.P.T.

Athletic Trainer
Assistant Professor of Physical Education
Southern Illinois University
Carbondale, Illinois

C H A R L E S   C   T H O M A S   •   P U B L I S H E R
Springfield   •   Illinois   •   U.S.A.

Published and Distributed Throughout the World by
CHARLES C THOMAS • PUBLISHER
BANNERSTONE HOUSE
301-327 East Lawrence Avenue, Springfield, Illinois, U.S.A.
NATCHEZ PLANTATION HOUSE
735 North Atlantic Boulevard, Fort Lauderdale, Florida, U.S.A.

With THOMAS BOOKS *careful attention is given to all details of
manufacturing and design. It is the Publisher's desire to present books
that are satisfactory as to their physical qualities and artistic possibilities
and appropriate for their particular use.* THOMAS BOOKS *will be true
to those laws of quality that assure a good name and good will.*

Printed in the United States of America
0-5

*Dedicated to my wife, Jane,
and to my four children*

Acknowledgments

THE AUTHOR wishes to express his sincere appreciation to those who gave freely of their time and assistance to help with this book.

The author is indebted to Fred Orlofsky, Charles Ehrlich, Craig Anderson, Bill Lepsi, Pete Hemmerling, Stewart Smith, Larry Kristoff, and other outstanding athletes at Southern Illinois University who kindly consented to pose and demonstrate the exercises for the pictures in the book. Larry Kristoff was one of Southern Illinois University's most outstanding wrestlers. He was a member of the United States Olympic Team in 1964 and 1968, represented the United States in the World Games five different years, and was National A.A.U. heavyweight wrestling champion ten times.

The author wishes to express appreciation to Robert "Rip" Stokes and Kenneth Garen for their help in the photography used in the manuscript.

R.R.S.

Contents

CONDITIONING FOR WRESTLING

Introduction

Wrestling is probably the most difficult sport to condition the body of all competitive athletics. It is a constant, season-long battle for the wrestler to keep his weight down and his strength at a near maximum. When cutting weight constantly, it is difficult to maintain one's strength. Many coaches have their wrestlers cut too much weight so that they have no strength at a lower weight class. Many wrestlers can't make the team at one weight class and cut their weight, sometimes as much as two weight classes, in order to wrestle. But usually they are too weak to win at the lower weight class. No one knows the long-range effects of cutting weight that may be injurious to one's health.

Some coaches and many wrestlers believe that wrestling itself will increase strength and maintain one's good physical condition. This we know is not true. Each day of wrestling the wrestler receives new contusions, muscle strains, sprains, and abrasions. His strength drops off quickly following contusions, sprains, and strains. If he does not work on resistive strength exercise almost daily he will get weaker in certain areas as the season goes on. Most wrestlers are weaker at the end of the season than they were at the beginning of the season if they do not work on strength exercise during the season.

Without a supervised strength program the only way wrestlers gain in strength is through growth and maturity from junior high through college.

All wrestlers in every weight class should be put on a supervised strength program according to their individual needs. There is no cure-all program that can be designed that will fit the needs of every wrestler. The author will try in this book to help the coach set up a program for the pre-season, regular season and off-season to fit the needs of each wrestler on his squad.

Conditioning for Wrestling

WE KNOW from experience and research in all sports the stronger boy is usually the better athlete. He is better for several reasons. With great strength he has more endurance, speed, agility, greater or faster reaction time, and usually with his exceptional muscle strength he has fewer injuries.

Wrestling fundamentals, techniques, and experience go a long way towards winning wrestling matches. All things being equal when both wrestlers have had good fundamentals and experience, the strong wrestler will win the majority of matches.

The strong wrestler can make mistakes or bad moves and still get out of trouble. The weaker wrestler who makes a bad move will usually get in trouble, lose points and perhaps the match.

There are many minor injuries throughout the season that handicap the wrestler. Each time he gets on the mat he receives a new injury. He may receive trauma to the thigh for a contusion, a sprained thumb, overstretched ligaments in the knee, or a neck strain from bridging on one six- or eight-minute match. For the next couple days he cannot get back on the mat because of his bruise on the thigh and the twisted knee. He cannot run because of pain and weakness in his leg, and the sprained thumb and strained neck prohibit much exercise for the upper body. Through disuse for a couple days the strength drops off in his legs and upper body. Not only does he lose strength, but also a great deal of cardiovascular endurance since he cannot run.

If he does not do some type of resistive exercise to regain muscle strength in his weak leg, he may be twenty to thirty pounds weaker in his leg. He cannot be as effective the next time he wrestles with this loss in strength. Favoring the weak leg, he may reinjure the leg or some other part of the body. This is the typical injury pattern that shortens many wrestling seasons and careers for wrestlers every year.

Wrestlers must do resistive strength exercises every day during wrestling season. Following every injury, minor and major, the wrestler must do prescribed resistive exercise (isometric or isotonic) to regain normal strength, with the strength even in both legs, before he gets back on the mat.

There are very few wrestlers who will work much on strength exercise during the season or off-season without direct orders from the coach. If he doesn't stand there and count for them they just will not do resistive exercise long enough to gain much strength. All athletes are a little lazy, except for the champion, and they will only exercise as much as the coach makes them exercise. There are many, many athletes with great talent, but they will not make the sacrifice to be a champion. There are also many who have drive and determination but no direction. If we could get these athletes on a prescribed strength and cardiovascular program according to their needs, we would have many more champions.

Every wrestler from junior high through college should work at least ten minutes every day on strength exercise during the season. In the off-season the wrestler should work at least three days a week for an hour a day on resistive exercise on all weak or underdeveloped muscle groups. He must be sure to strengthen last season's injured area. In the pre-season program each wrestler should work five days a week for thirty minutes a day on strength exercises along with his cardiovascular endurance

4

work, flexibility, agility, and wrestling skills with the rest of his conditioning program.

When the regular season begins he will go back to his ten minutes of resistive strength exercise daily as part of the regular workout. All this exercise should be prescribed by the trainer or coach according to the wrestlers individual needs. He must run, run, run to improve and maintain his cardiovascular endurance. Running will include some distance work (one to two miles daily) and many short sprints (10 to 25 yards) with little rest in between the sprints.

Off-season Conditioning

The off-season is the time for working on the weak areas in the body for high school and college wrestlers. They must have extreme range in all joints. Flexibility in the back, legs, chest, and shoulders is a must for all wrestlers who want to have good skill and prevent injuries. A broomstick cut 42 to 48 inches in length can be used in the exercises for the chest and shoulders shown on pages 31 and 32.

On wrestlers, the low back and the muscles on the back of the legs (hamstrings) should be loose and stretched out. All wrestlers should be able to lay their palms flat on the floor with the knees straight and the feet together. Use the exercises on page 33 for the back of the leg stretch. See the pictures below and check your flexibility.

Can you lay your palms flat on the floor? If you cannnot touch your palms to the floor, or if you are tight in other areas, use the shower room stretching procedure on page 33. Keep stretching daily until you can lay your palms flat on the floor. Then keep stretching your hamstrings and back daily to stay stretched out throughout the year. You lose running speed and wrestling moves quickly when your hamstrings and your low back are tight.

Wrestlers who are loose and have good flexibility in the low back, shoulders, legs and in the rest of the body usually do not get injured as often as the wrestlers who are tight.

The off-season is also the time to strengthen the whole body and restrengthen the injured areas of the body. Follow all the strength exercises in the following pages, both isotonic and isometric, and improve your wrestling ability for the coming season.

STRETCHING FOR FLEXIBILITY

The wrestler must work for extremes in range of motion in all joints. His shoulders must be loose and flexible. All wrestlers should be able to lay their palms flat on the floor, bending over with the knees straight. They should be able to sit back on their heels and lay their shoulders back on the mat without discomfort. They should stretch the muscles on the inside of the thighs (adductors) daily and work until they can do the split as the gymnasts do in free exercise. See the pictures on the following pages.

Stretching should be routine for all wrestlers. They must stretch daily to maintain and gain flexibility before every workout. They must work even harder at stretching if they have tightness in any area in order to increase their range of motion. The older college wrestler must do more stretching exercise every year to maintain his flexibility and to warm up before participation. This is due many times to

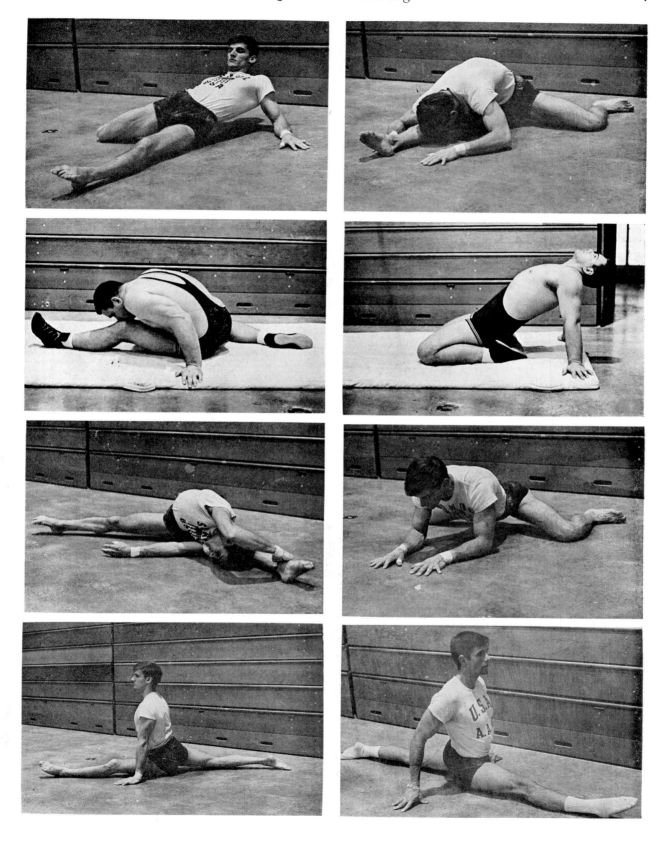

old injuries, scar tissue, and weak muscles. Each year it takes longer and much more effort to get into top physical condition and to maintain this top physical condition.

Every good wrestler must have great strength, endurance strength, agility, cardiovascular endurance and extremes in flexibility. Flexibility in the back, shoulders, arms, chest, legs, and ankles is an absolute necessity for wrestlers. All good wrestlers are very flexible.

Check your flexibility with the pictures below.

Face to Shins

Back Flexibility

Heel Cords

Adductors of the Hip

After checking the pictures of flexibility, if you have tightness in any of the areas, it is best to do your stretching daily, in the shower room or immediately after the shower. See the stretching exercises using shower room procedure on page 10.

You may also increase your flexibility by using ice massage. For example, if you have tight hamstrings (back of the legs), rub the legs with ice for ten to fifteen minutes. This will get very cold and will relax the muscles after the massage. Then begin slowly to stretch the back of the legs. Do not use a ballistic stretch by bobbing up and down hard, forcing a stretch. Bend over slowly and stretch, hold the muscle on a stretch, and come back up and relax (see back of the leg stretching [hamstrings] on pages 9 & 33). Repeat the ice massage or shower room technique in any tight area until you have the desired range of motion and flexibility. Stretch daily to maintain this flexibility. Work towards attaining the flexibility shown on the pictures.

STRETCHING EXERCISE PROCEDURE

1. Stretching exercise should be done daily along with isometric exercise and isotonic exercise.

2. When there is tightness in any area, in order to gain in range of motion, it is better to stretch after some type of heat has been applied, or ice massage for ten to fifteen minutes to the area being stretched. For example, there may be tightness in the low back and the back of the legs. This tightness limits the wrestler in sitting out and make it difficult to flex the body from the waist. Bend over in the shower and heat the area well, or rub ice on the area for ten to fifteen minutes. Then bend over slowly and stretch, holding the position for six seconds. Repeat the stretch, going down a little farther each time. Do not bob up and down to force a stretch as many individuals do — this may cause an injury by violently overstretching tight muscles. Follow the stretching procedure under number 4 and 5 below.

3. Where extreme tightness exists, stretching may be done in two different ways to increase the circulation and relax the tight muscles.

4. Stretching may be done after heat in the following manner: (a) Allow hot water to heat the part well in the shower. (b) Stretch in the same method used in exercising. (c) Stretch as far as you can until you feel a little pain. (d) Hold this position for six seconds; relax six seconds; try to go a little farther again and hold for six seconds; relax six seconds; try to go a little farther again and hold for six seconds; relax. See the pictures on pages 10 and 33.

5. Stretching may be done after cold in the following manner: (a) Rub the area with ice for ten or fifteen minutes. The cold may be a little uncomfortable for about one to two minutes, and then the area becomes numb. (b) Stretch in the same method used in exercising. (c) The cold increases the circulation and the tight muscles relax when you stop the ice massage. (d) Stretch as far as you can until you feel a little pain. (e) Hold this position for six seconds; relax six seconds; try to go a little farther again and hold six seconds; relax six seconds; try to go a little farther again and hold six seconds; relax.

6. Repeat the same procedure in stretching all tight areas in the body. Repeat several times daily until you gain complete range of motion.

7. Stretch every day to maintain complete range of motion.

STRETCHING EXERCISES USING SHOWER ROOM PROCEDURE

1. Heel Cord Stretch

a. Hold six seconds — relax — repeat three to six times.

2. Hamstring Stretch

a. Hold six seconds — relax — repeat three to six times.

3. Back Stretch

a. Hold six seconds — relax — repeat three to six times.

4. Back and Shoulder Stretch (Hang by Hands)

a. Tilt pelvis forward and backward.
b. Hold six seconds each way — relax — repeat three to six times.

5. Back and Side Stretch (Both Sides)

a. Hold six seconds — relax — repeat three to six times.
b. Stretch both sides.

6. Chest and Shoulder Stretch

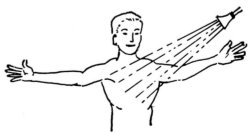

a. Hold six seconds — relax — repeat three to six times.

7. Chest and Shoulder Stretch Overhead

a. Hold six seconds — relax — repeat three to six times.

8. Shoulder Rotators Stretch (Internal and External Rotators

a. Rotate shoulders outward — hold six seconds — relax — repeat three to six times.
b. Rotate shoulders inward — hold six seconds — relax — repeat three to six times.
c. Also turn back to shower.

9. Wrist Stretch (Flexing and Extending)

a. Stretch wrist down — hold six seconds — relax — repeat three to six times.
b. Stretch wrist back — hold six seconds — relax — repeat three to six times.
c. Stretch both wrists.

10. Biceps Stretch

a. Hold elbow straight — pull back on wrist pushing elbow forward.
b. Hold six seconds — relax — repeat three to six times.
c. Stretch both arms.

STRENGTH TESTING

The coach or trainer should give all of the wrestlers a strength test at the beginning of pre-season conditioning and at the end of the wrestling season. Then each wrestler should be given an individual strength resistive exercise program according to his strength needs as shown by the strength test. All exercises should be prescribed and supervised.

With a two-man exercise program the coach or trainer can test the muscle strength of each individual muscle group. Each wrestler and wrestling team will require different exercises. In general, all wrestlers must have strong hands, wrists, arms, shoulders, back, legs and the entire body. Each wrestler will have to work on a different area, so the coach should include strength work in his daily practice sessions for each wrestler according to his weakness.

In the off-season, the coach should mark the exercises in the book which he wants each individual wrestler to be sure to do to strengthen his weak knee, shoulder, wrist, or any weak area. The wrestler will take his book home and follow his prescribed exercise program. Each wrestler will spend more time strengthening his weak areas. The whole wrestling team will do all the exercises for all wrestlers suggested in the book.

When school begins the coach or trainer will retest to be sure the wrestler strengthened last year's injured shoulder or knee before beginning the pre-season conditioning program.

The coach should know his team and try to prevent injuries rather than try to rehabilitate them after they are injured. Freshman wrestlers on both high school and college wrestling teams will have to spend more time on strength exercises than the rest of the squad during the daily practice schedule. Some years this may not be necessary if the team has a strong freshman group. However, most members will have some weak area from old injuries or areas that are just underdeveloped. The coach should always give his team a muscle strength test to determine the weak members. He must remember that muscle girth is no indication of strength. The wrestler may look strong, but have no strength due to an old injury.

By comparing the muscle strength of one extremity with the opposite extremity, one can detect weakness to some degree. For example, to test the strength of the big muscles over the point of the shoulder (deltoids), see exercises 1, 2, and 3 under Shoulder and Arm Exercises on pages 61-62. Where there is unequal strength when lifting the arms forward, the man giving the resistance can easily distinguish which arm is the weaker. Raise the arms to the side and resist; push the arms backward and resist. In this manner one can test the muscle strength of the deltoid group. Should there be a weakness, continue the exercises on both extremities until the strength appears to be the same. Then continue the exercise daily throughout the season to increase or maintain the strength. The stronger wrestler is usually the better wrestler, and he has fewer injuries.

No one knows what is normal strength in any area of the body or for any particular body weight. Due to variables such as age, weight, height, body build, length of the lever, previous activity or sports, diet, and many others, we cannot set up norms. Most wrestlers are strong, well-built, and on the lean side due to cutting weight. They must increase their strength and keep their body weight close to their weight class at all times.

Many wrestlers have weak backs on one side due to previous injuries and due to the sport itself with repeated bridging and twisting to avoid being pinned and to try to escape. To check strength in the lower back, see Back Exercises number 6 and 7 on pages 73-74. It will be easy to determine muscle weakness to some degree. Continue the exercise until both sides of the back seem to have the same strength and there is no pain. Then continue the exercise daily throughout the season to increase or maintain the strength. The strength drops off quickly in old injured areas. You can test the muscle strength in the whole body by comparing the strength of one extremity with the other, or one side of the body with the other side.

Muscle strength both before and after an exercise program can best be evaluated with strength testing equipment. There are many variables in manual strength testing, but where there is no testing apparatus, the comparison method described above appears to be the best. The author now has a muscle testing device on the market, The Spackman Muscle Testing Unit.* The research on this unit was done at Southern Illinois University.

By testing muscle strength it is possible with The Spackman Muscle Testing device to tell if the wrestler is strong or weak. Should an injury occur, one can tell how much strength has been lost due to the injury.

Following a corrective exercise program for the injured area, a comparison can then be made of the results of the tests done before the injury. One can tell when he is back to normal strength. We do not let the wrestler go back to wrestling until the strength is equal in both

---

*Manufactured by La Berne Manufacturing Co., 819 Leesburg Road, Columbia, S.C. 29205.

legs, both sides of the back, or wherever the injury has occurred. The muscle testing unit acts as a motivator to anyone who is interested in gaining muscle strength. It takes all the

guesswork out of athletic injuries. We know when the strength is back and when the wrestler is ready to go back on the mat.

Muscle Testing Unit

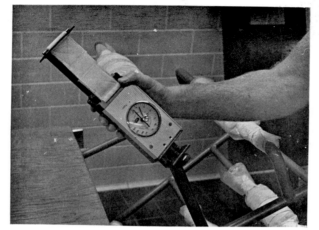

Testing Back Strength

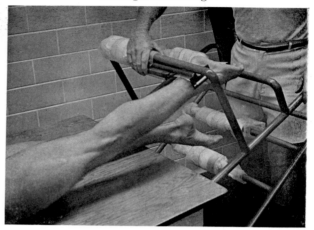

WRIST ROLLER

To strengthen the forearm, wrist, and hand, all wrestlers should make the following simple device and use it daily. Take an old baseball bat and cut off a piece about fourteen inches long. Drill a hole in the center of the bat handle. Cut a piece of rope five feet long and thread it through the hole. Tie a brick or a weight on the end of the rope (see page 36).

Grasp the bat in the hands and hold it out at shoulder height. Slowly twist the bat and wind

the rope in order to roll the brick up to the bat handle. Alternate one hand and then the other, reaching way under, and roll the wrist over the top very slowly. Slowly lower the weight the same way. Roll the weight up and down slowly five times daily. When five repetitions become an easy task, add another brick or more weight. When you finish the exercise with the wrist roller, be sure to stretch the wrist to maintain flexibility.

WEIGHTED BAR

Here is another simple device a wrestler can make to strengthen the forearm, wrist, and hand. Find an old baseball bat and load the end with weight. This may be done yourself by drilling a six to eight-inch hole in the end of the bat about an inch in diameter and driving a solid piece of metal into the hole. You may also use melted lead to fill the hole in the bat. If you have no weighted bat, you may tie a brick or a weight on a broomstick, an old golf club, or use a weighted bar.

The following wrist and forearm exercises should be done daily with the weighted bar or bat in order to increase and maintain strength.

If the bar is too heavy, slide the the hand up the handle and exercise from this position. As strength increases, move the hand to the end of the bat. Exercise both hands and wrists.

You should experience no pain during the exercise; if you do, you have a weak or an injured wrist. Should you have pain during exercise, you will keep the wrist sore, and it will remain weak. Slide your hand up the bat so that you can exercise without pain (see exercises on page 35). Exercise with the weighted bat or bar in the off-season, pre-season, and daily during the regular season. Strong hands and wrists are a must for all wrestlers.

MEDI EXERCISE BALL

If you want to be good at anything, you have to work at it constantly. Wrestlers have a lot of contusions, sprains and strains from overstretching the shoulder muscles every time they get on the mat. All wrestlers should have a medi exercise ball* or a dumbbell to stretch and strengthen the muscles of the shoulder, forearm, wrist, chest, and back. The medi exercise ball is a moulded ball that weighs between three and four pounds. If you are handy, perhaps you can make your own medi exercise ball or use a solid dumbbell.

When beginning medi ball exercises, three to four pounds is enough weight. As the strength increases the wrestler may increase the weight gradually to perhaps a high of ten pounds according to his wrestling weight.

These exercises were originated by Bob Bauman, Trainer with the St. Louis Cardinals Baseball Team. Bob has rehabilitated and strengthened more arms and shoulders than any trainer in the country. The author had the pleasure of working with Bob Bauman for several years when he was head trainer for the old St. Louis Browns in the American League.

The following exercises should be done with both arms at least three times a week in the off-season, and daily during pre-season and the regular wrestling season.

---

*Distributed by Van Sickle Company, 2115 59th Street, St. Louis, Missouri 63110, for $6.50.

Medi Exercise Ball Exercises

Forward Swing

1. Forward and Backward Swings

   a. Place the left hand on the left knee and bend forward at the waist. The feet are spread apart about 24 inches.

   b. Grasp the ball in the right hand with the arm hanging loosely in front of the body.

   c. Swing the ball forward overhead and backward, letting the ball carry the arm.

   d. Repeat ten to twenty forward and backward swings until the muscles are warm and loose.

   e. Repeat the same exercise, raising the ball forward and backward very slowly five times, getting a good stretch in each direction.

   f. Repeat the exercise with the left arm.

Backward Swing

Lateral Swing Across the Chest

Lateral Swing Back to the Right

2. **Lateral Swing Side to Side**

   a. Place the left hand on the left knee and bend forward at the waist. The feet are spread apart about 24 inches.

   b. Grasp the ball or dumbbell in the right hand, with the arm hanging loosely in front of the body.

   c. Swing the ball across the chest to the left and back up to the right, letting the ball carry the arm.

   d. Repeat ten to twenty lateral swings from side to side until the muscles are warm and loose.

   e. Repeat the same exercise, raising the ball from side to side very slowly five times, getting a good stretch in each direction.

   f. Repeat the exercise with the left arm.

Circle Swing to the Right

Circle Swing Forward

3. Circle Swing

a. Place the left hand on the left knee and bend forward at the waist. The feet are spread about 24 inches.

b. Grasp the ball or dumbbell in the right hand, with the arm hanging loosely in front of the body.

c. Swing the ball, making a circle in a clockwise direction for ten circles. Swing the ball in a circle in a counterclockwise direction for ten circles.

d. Repeat the same exercise, making a clockwise circle very slowly five times. Repeat a counterclockwise circle very slowly five times, getting a good stretch in each direction.

e. Repeat the exercise with the left arm.

Circle Swing to the Left

Starting Position

Overhead Stretch

4. Overhead Stretch

a. Stand straight with the shoulders level, feet spread about 24 inches apart. Bend the elbow to 90 degrees and raise the arm to shoulder level.

b. Grasp the ball or dumbbell in the right hand in a perpendicular position.

c. Raise the ball straight upward, extending the elbow. Keep the shoulders level and push as high as possible, getting a good stretch along the arm and side of the chest.

d. Return to the starting position.

e. Repeat five to ten overhead stretches, trying to go a little higher on each stretch.

f. Repeat the exercise with the left arm.

Shoulder External Rotation

5. Shoulder Rotation
(External and Internal)

   a. Stand straight with the shoulders level, feet spread apart about 24 inches. Bend the elbow to 90 degrees and raise the arm to shoulder level.

   b. Grasp the ball or dumbbell in the right hand. Slowly rotate the arm externally, as you do in throwing, bending the wrist backward. Get a good stretch in the shoulder.

   c. Slowly rotate the arm internally, as you do in throwing, bending the wrist forward. Keep the wrist and elbow at shoulder level. Get a good stretch in the shoulder.

   d. Repeat external and internal rotation of the shoulder five times, getting a good stretch.

   e. Repeat the exercise with the left arm.

   f. Repeat the same exercise, lying on a table, keeping the wrist and elbow at shoulder level while rotating the arm externally and internally stretching the shoulder.

Shoulder Internal Rotation

Conditioning for Wrestling

Wrist Flexion

Wrist Extension

Elbow Flexion

6. Biceps and Wrist Stretching and Strengthening

a. Stand straight with the shoulders level, feet spread about 24 inches apart. Raise the right arm to shoulder level with the palm up. The left hand is placed under the right upper arm to hold the shoulder and elbow level.

b. Grasp the ball or dumbbell in the right hand and slowly bend the wrist upward and downward, getting a good stretch. Slowly bend the elbow upward and downward, getting a good stretch. Slowly rotate the forearm inwardly and outwardly (supination and pronation), getting a good stretch.

c. Repeat each exercise of the wrist, forearm and elbow five times, getting a good stretch.

d. Repeat the same exercise slowly with the left arm.

Elbow Extension

Wrist Pronation (Palm Down)

Wrist Supination (Palm Up)

CARDIOVASCULAR EXERCISE

Cardiovascular endurance is very very necessary for the wrestler. He needs this type of endurance to go at a near all-out effort for six- or nine-minute matches. Speed, agility, balance, timing and all the qualities necessary to be a good wrestler improve when the wrestler has good cardiovascular endurance. Here are three ways you can improve and maintain your cardiovascular endurance in the pre-season, regular season, and off-season conditioning programs.

Make yourself a box or a stool twenty inches high, twenty inches wide, and twenty inches deep. This exercise is called The Brouha Step Test,[1] or The Harvard Step Test. In this exercise the wrestler steps up and down on a twenty-inch box thirty times a minute for five minutes. On the count of one, step up on the box with the left foot; step up with the right foot on the count of two; then step down with the left foot; and on the count of four, step down with the right foot. After two and one half minutes, change and lead with the right foot. As this exercise becomes easy, you may add weight to the feet, wear a weighted vest, or hold dumb-

bells in each hand (see pictures below).

Pulse rates may be taken before and after exercise; improvement is shown by a lowered resting pulse rate after five minutes of exercise and by a quickened recovery to a resting pulse rate after five minutes of exercise.

In the first few days, when beginning the step test, you may start out at a cadence of twenty-four steps per minute for three minutes. When five minutes is easy at twenty-four steps per minute, step up the cadence to thirty steps per minute (see the pictures on page 24).

Another cardiovascular exercise you may do for developing endurance is The Carlson Fatigue Test.[2] It is easier on the feet to do this exercise on the wrestling mat or on a soft surface. The exercise consists of running in place as fast as you can for ten seconds, then resting ten seconds; this is repeated for ten bouts — or the equivalent of ten 100-yard dashes in ten seconds, with ten seconds rest between each dash. Count each time your right foot contacts the floor and record this number after each ten-second run. As a check on your prog-

Step Test with Weights in Hands

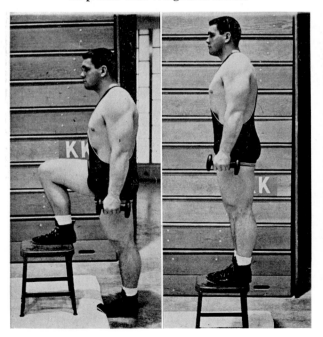

Step Test Wearing Weighted Vest

ress, five measures of pulse rate are taken: (a) before exercise; (b) ten seconds after exercise; (c) two minutes after exercise; (d) four minutes after exercise; (e) six minutes after exercise. A quick return to normal pulse rate after exercise and an increase in number of times the right foot hits the floor give indications of your improvement in conditioning.

Rope-skipping is another good cardiovascular exercise for the wrestler that may be done outdoors or indoors in the gym. There are many methods of skipping rope — alternating on one foot, and then on the other foot; on both feet; or the boxer's shuffle as when boxers skip rope. In this latter method you only jump high enough for the rope to clear your feet.

Timing your rope-skipping is one method of measuring your improvement. Skip rope for one minute and rest for one minute. This may be repeated for ten one-minute periods with one minute rests between. Should this become too easy, increase the number to fifteen one-minute periods, or hold two- or four-pound dumbbells in each hand when skipping. You may also add ankle weights to the ankle or wear a weighted vest when skipping for more resistance.

[1]Brouha, I: The step test: A simple method of measuring physical fitness for muscular work in young men. *Research Quarterly, 14*:31–36, March 1943.
[2]Carlson, H. C.: Fatigue curve test. *Research Quarterly, 16*:169–175, October 1945.

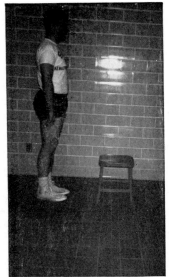

1

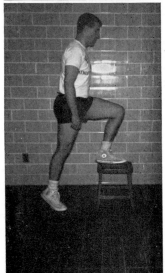

2

3

4

5

Brouha Step Test

1. Starting position.
2. Step up with left foot.
3. Step up with right foot.
4. Step down with left foot.
5. Step down with right foot.

NOTE: High school boys and boys with short legs use a lower stool (15 inches high).

Skipping Rope with Ankle Weights and Hand Weights

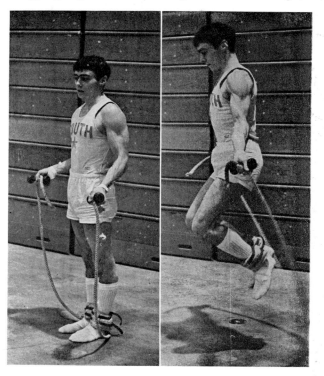

These three exercises do not replace running They only supplement running when you cannot get out and run. Many wrestling teams will skip rope or use The Carlson Fatigue Test and The Harvard Step Test daily as part of their daily workout. They are excellent substitutes in the off-season and pre-season when you don't have time to get out and run a mile or two or do repeat sprints. They are also great when the weather is too cold, snowy or rainy.

Running is a part of wrestling just as running is a must for the shot put, discus and hammer throwers in track. Wrestlers must run daily as part of their workout. They run a mile or two daily — not just jogging, but running as fast and as hard as they can for the mile. Time your running and work towards improving your time. It is better to run repeat 220's and repeat 440's than to just go out and jog.

Use a stop watch and time your sprints or distance running. Always work towards improving your time. Your times will improve as your condition improves. In the pre-season all wrestlers should run for distance and do many short sprints to improve their cardiovascular endurance. In the regular season they will still run daily to maintain their cardiovascular endurance, but will work more on their strength, flexibility, agility, balance, timing, and other wrestling skills.

STRENGTH EXERCISE

In the pre-season, regular season, and off-season all wrestlers must do strength exercises to increase and maintain their strength and to stay "stretched out." Thirty-six-second isometric pull-ups, push-ups, and shoulder dips are excellent to maintain and increase shoulder and arm strength. More resistance may be added as these exercises become easy.

Pull-ups

Wrestlers should do pull-ups every day. Most wrestlers can do fifteen to twenty-five pull-ups with very little effort. They do these to maintain endurance strength. To increase strength, pull-ups may be done isometrically by holding for six seconds at different points throughout the pull-up. To add more resistance, weights may be applied by wearing a weighted vest or by holding a dumbbell (10, 15, or 25 pounds) between your knees as you do your pull-up. A partner can take the weight as you finish.

Pull-ups should be done with different grips — the palms away from the body and the palms facing the body. Thirty-six-second pull-ups are done in the following manner: (a) pull up flexing the elbows about 15 degrees and hold for six seconds; (b) pull up flexing the elbows to 90 degrees and hold for six seconds; (c) pull up looking over the bar and hold for six seconds; (d) lower slowly to 90 degrees of elbow flexion and hold for six seconds; (e) lower slowly to 15 degrees of elbow flexion and hold for six seconds; (f) lower to complete elbow extension and hold, stretching for six seconds.

Do at least three pull-ups daily for thirty-six seconds in the off-season, using each grip to maintain your shoulder and arm strength. Keep adding resistance if you want to increase your

Weighted Vest

Weight Between the Knees

strength. In the pre-season and regular season do many more thirty-six-second pull-ups with more resistance to continue increasing your strength. Be sure to use the different hand grips while holding the bar.

Thirty-six-second Pull-ups

Push-ups

Wrestlers do push-ups daily to strengthen the fingers, wrists, arms, and chest: (a) with hands close together, forming a triangle with the fingers and thumbs under the chest; (b) with hands wide outside the shoulders; (c) or with hands directly under the shoulders. Push-ups may also be done with the hands on two chairs, lowering the body between the chairs to get a good stretch across the chest.

Hands on the Chairs

Lower the Body Between the Chairs

Do fifteen to twenty-five push-ups daily all year long, slowly pushing up and down. More resistance may be added by putting one's feet up on a chair with the hands on the floor. Thirty-six-second isometric push-ups may also be done as in pull-ups and shoulder dips. Many wrestlers do push-ups on their finger tips to strengthen their fingers and wrists. Other wrestlers use the twenty-pound weighted vest to add more resistance (see the pictures below).

Shoulder Dips

The wrestler does shoulder dips daily on the parallel bars or between two tables. The thirty-six-second shoulder dip is one of the better methods of developing arm, shoulder, and chest strength.

Thirty-six-second isometric shoulder dips are done in the following manner: (a) with the elbows completely extended, lower the body flexing the elbows about 15 degrees and hold for six seconds; (b) slowly lower the body flexing the elbows to 90 degrees and hold for six seconds; (c) lower the body to complete elbow flexion and hold for six seconds; (d) push the body up to 90 degrees of elbow flexion and hold for six seconds; (e) push the body up to 15 degrees of elbow flexion and hold for six seconds; (f) push the body as far as possible, completely extending the elbows, and hold for six seconds.

Do thirty-six-second isometric shoulder dips daily throughout the year. Pre-seasonally and during the regular season the wrestler should do many more thirty-six-second shoulder dips. More resistance may be added by holding a dumbbell between your knees or by wearing a twenty-pound weighted vest while doing the shoulder dips in order to increase shoulder and arm strength (see the pictures below).

Most wrestlers can do fifteen to twenty-five repetitions of shoulder dips without too much difficulty. If you cannot do twenty shoulder dips, practice daily until you can.

WARM-UP EXERCISE

In wrestling, warm-up exercises are an individual problem. It is essential for wrestlers of all ages to be thoroughly warmed up and stretched out before getting on the mats. Break a good sweat before you attempt to wrestle. Naturally the young wrestler in junior high or high school will not need as much warm-up as the older college wrestler. The heavier wrestlers need more warm-up and stretching than the light weight wrestlers.

Each year the individual wrestler will find he has to spend more time stretching and warming up the muscles before performing. The wrestler is continually learning new moves and holds. With each new move or hold he may overstretch, strain, bruise, or tear muscle fibers. Every time he injures muscle fibers there will be some soreness and pain. He must exercise daily to pump blood into the muscles to relieve the stiffness and pain before beginning his workout.

How much warm-up the wrestler will do will depend on the weather (hot or cold), his age, old injuries, his present state of physical fitness, muscle tightness, pain, and many more variables. Warming up is an individual problem, but be sure you are warm and loose in order to avoid injury before you wrestle. See the stretching exercises and warm-up exercises on pages 31 through 56.

Stretching Exercises

Chest and Shoulder Stretch

1. Standing
   a. Hold a broomstick (42-45 in.) in front of the body, in the palms of the hands.
   b. Keep the elbows straight.
   c. Lift the broomstick forward and over the head slowly.
   d. Stretch for six seconds and slowly return; relax.
   e. Repeat three times, stretching a little farther each time.

3. Standing
   a. Hold a broomstick in front of the body.
   b. Push the broomstick up in front of the body on one side.
   c. Keep the elbow straight on the overhead arm.
   d. Stretch for six seconds and return to the front of the body.
   e. Push the broomstick up in front of the body to the other side.
   f. Repeat three times, stretching a little farther each time.

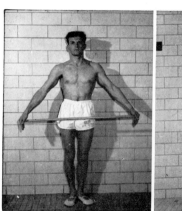  

2. Standing
   a. Hold a broomstick out to the side of the body.
   b. Keep the elbow straight on the overhead arm.
   c. Push the broomstick up to the side slowly.
   d. Stretch for six seconds and slowly push the broomstick up to the other side, stretch for six seconds.
   e. Repeat three times, stretching a little farther each time.

4. Standing
   a. Hold a broomsick behind the body.
   b. Keep the elbows straight.
   c. Push the broomstick backward as high as possible.
   d. Keep the body straight. Do not bend forward.
   e. Stretch for six seconds and return to the starting position.

 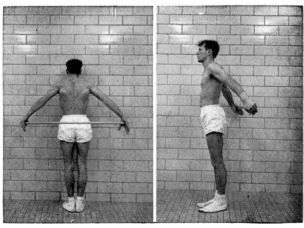

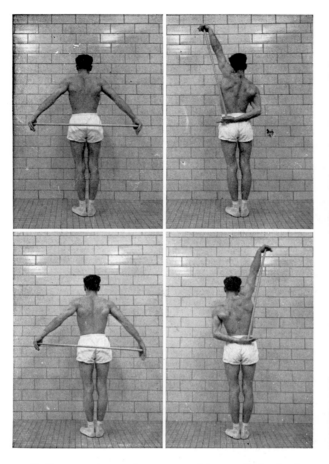

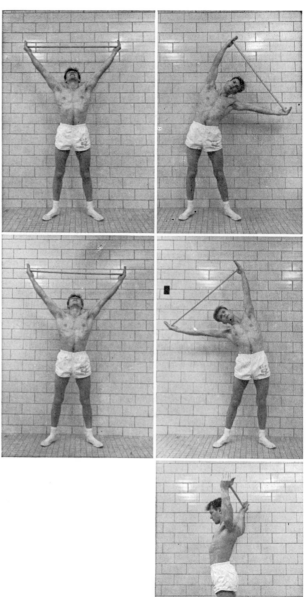

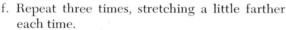

f. Repeat three times, stretching a little farther each time.

5. Standing
   a. Hold a broomstick behind the body.
   b. Push the broomstick up to the side.
   c. Keep the elbow straight on the overhead arm.
   d. Stretch for six seconds and return to the starting position.
   e. Push the broomstick up to the other side.
   f. Stretch for six seconds and return; relax.
   g. Repeat three times, stretching a little farther each time.

6. Standing
   a. Hold a broomstick overhead in the palms of the hands.
   b. Keep the elbows straight. The feet are about 18 inches apart.
   c. Bend sideward as far as possible, keeping the elbows straight.
   d. Stretch for six seconds and return to the starting position.

   e. Bend sideward as far as possible to the other side.
   f. Stretch for six seconds and return to the starting position.
   g. Repeat three times, stretching a little farther each time.

7. Standing

   a. Hold a broomstick overhead in the palms of the hands.
   b. The shoulders are raised to 90 degrees, and the elbows are bent to 90 degrees.

c. Rotate the arms backward as far as possible.
d. Stretch for six seconds and return to the starting position.
e. Repeat three times, stretching a little farther each time (see pictures on page 19).

Back of the Leg Stretch (Hamstrings)

1. Standing

   a. Cross one leg in front of the other leg. The feet are close together.
   b. Hold the rear leg back with the front leg.
   c. Keep both knees straight.
   d. Bend over and touch the floor beside the feet.
   e. Stretch for six seconds and return.
   f. Place the other leg in front.
   g. Stretch for six seconds and return.
   h. Repeat three times with each leg forward, stretching a little farther each time.

2. Standing

   a. Cross one leg in front of the other leg. The feet are close together.
   b. Bend the elbows and fold the arms in front of the body up near the head.
   c. Bend over as far as possible and stretch out with the elbows.
   d. Stretch for six seconds and return.
   e. Repeat three times, bending and stretching a little farther each time.
   f. Place the other leg in front.
   g. Stretch for six seconds and return.
   h. Repeat three times, bending and stretching a little farther each time.

3. Standing

   a. Raise one leg on a table or a hurdle with the knee bent.
   b. Bend over and try to touch the floor beside the foot.
   c. Keep the leg and knee straight.
   d. Stretch for six seconds and return.
   e. Raise the other leg on the table.
   f. Bend over and try to touch the floor beside the foot.
   g. Stretch for six seconds and return. Try to put the palms flat on the floor.
   h. Repeat three times with each leg, stretching a little farther each time.

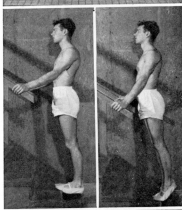

Heel Cord Stretch

1. Standing
   a. Step forward with the left leg.
   b. Keep the right leg back with the knee held straight.
   c. Bend the left knee and bring the body forward, keeping both feet pointing straight ahead.
   d. Keep the right heel on the floor and stretch the right heel cord for six seconds.
   e. Step forward with the right leg.
   f. Keep the left heel on the floor and stretch the left heel cord for six seconds.
   g. Repeat three times with each leg, stretching a little farther each time.

2. Standing on the stairs
   a. Stand with the balls of the feet on the edge of the stairs.
   b. Rise on the toes as high as possible, holding for six seconds.
   c. Drop down off the edge of the stairs, stretching the heel cords for six seconds.
   d. Rise up and down three times, stretching a little farther each time.

3. Standing
   a. Walk on the heels with the ball of the foot off the ground.
   b. Stretch the foot up hard, walking at least 30 yards; relax.
   c. Repeat three times, stretching a little farther each time.

4. Standing
   a. Place the hands against the wall at shoulder height.
   b. Keep the heels on the floor.
   c. Move backward until you feel a good stretch on the heel cords.
   d. Stretch the heel cords for six seconds.
   e. Repeat three times, stretching a little farther each time.

Wrist Stretching and Strengthening

1. Standing
   a. Raise the left arm straight out in front of the body.
   b. Bend the left wrist down with the palm of the hand forward.
   c. Grasp the left palm with the right hand, stretching the wrist down and back for six seconds.
   d. Repeat three times with each wrist, stretching a little farther each time.
   e. Turn the hand over and stretch the wrist the other way.
   f. Repeat three times with each wrist, stretching a little farther each time.

2. Standing (Weighted bar exercises)
   a. Hold a weighted bar in front of the body.
   b. Keep the elbow straight with the weight pointing toward the floor.
   c. Lift the weight up slowly, taking six seconds to raise.

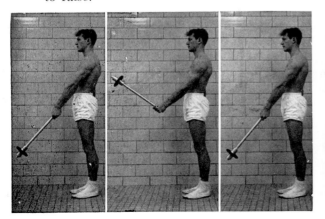

   d. Slowly lower the weight, taking six seconds to lower to the starting position.
   e. Repeat three times with each wrist.
   f. Add more weight when three repetitions become easy.

3. Standing
   a. Hold a weighted bar behind the body.
   b. Keep the elbow straight with the weight pointing toward the floor.
   c. Lift the weight up slowly, taking six seconds to raise.
   d. Slowly lower the weight, taking six seconds to lower to the starting position.
   e. Repeat three times with each wrist.
   f. Add more weight when three repetitions become easy.

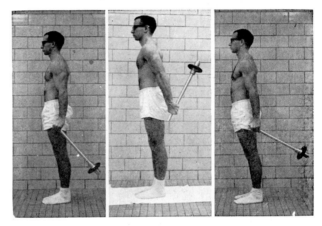

4. Standing
   a. Hold a weighted bar in front of the body with the elbow straight.

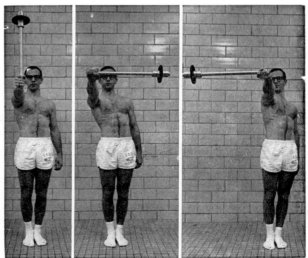

b. Raise the arm up straight in front of the body to shoulder height.

c. Slowly pronate (turn) the hand, lowering the weight to the inside, taking three seconds to lower. Keep the elbow straight.

d. Slowly return to the starting position taking three seconds to return.

e. Slowly supinate (turn) the hand, lowering the weight to the outside, taking three seconds to lower and three seconds to return.

f. Repeat three times with each wrist.

g. Add more weight when three repetitions become easy.

h. Do exercises 1, 2, 3, and 4 with weighted golf club daily (see page 35).

5. Standing

a. Hold a bar out in front of the body with a rope and a weight tied to the end.

b. Slowly roll the weight up on the bar. Keep the elbows straight.

c. Reach under the bar as far as possible and roll the wrist over the top.

d. Slowly roll the weight down to the starting position.

e. Repeat three times rolling the weight up and down.

f. Five pounds is a good starting weight.

g. Add more weight when three repetitions becomes easy.

WARM-UP EXERCISES

1. Side Straddle Hop Bend

2. Trunk Rotation — Standing with a Broomstick in Elbows Behind Back

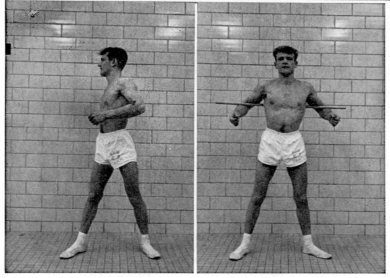

3. Alternate Toe Touch

4. Side Bender

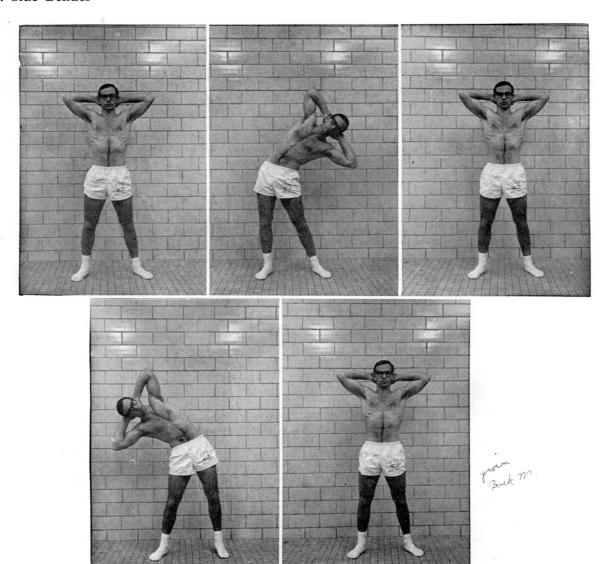

5. Trunk Rotation

6. Burpee with a Push-up

7. Leg Extension Sideward from a Squat Position

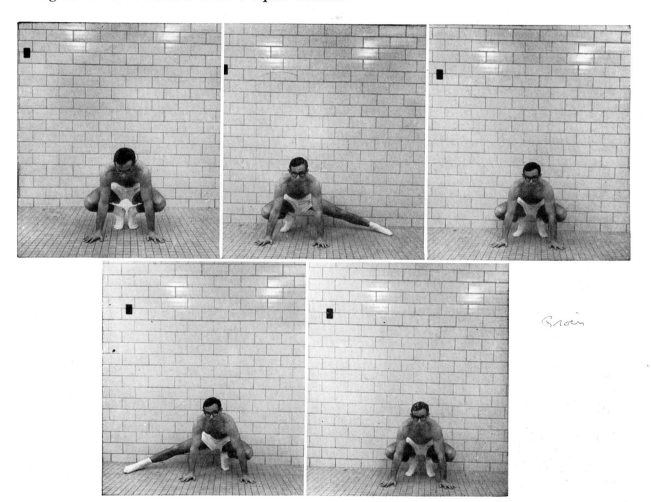

8. Sit-up with a Partner

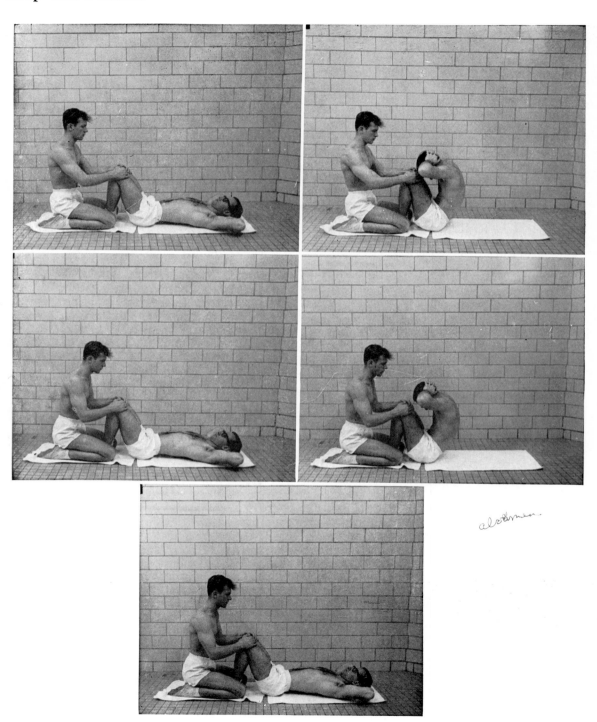

9. Alternate Leg Lift (Hamstring Stretch)

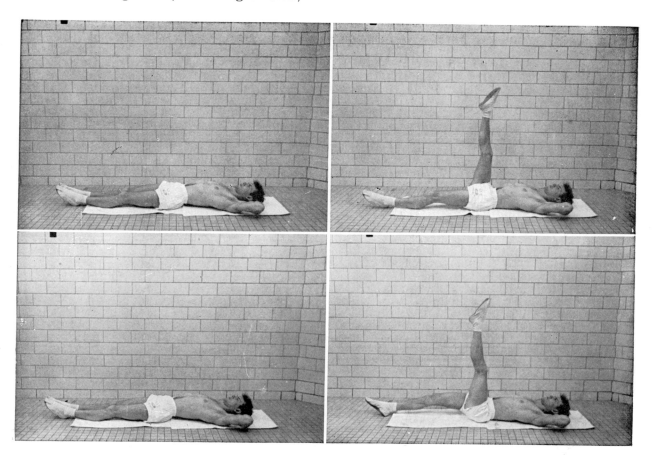

10. Alternate Knee to Chest

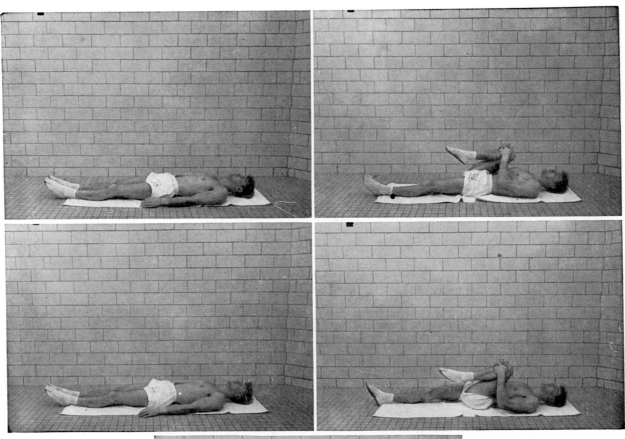

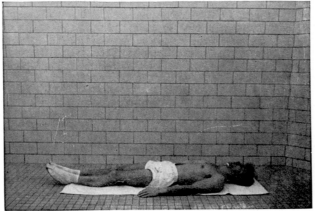

11. Double Knee to Chest

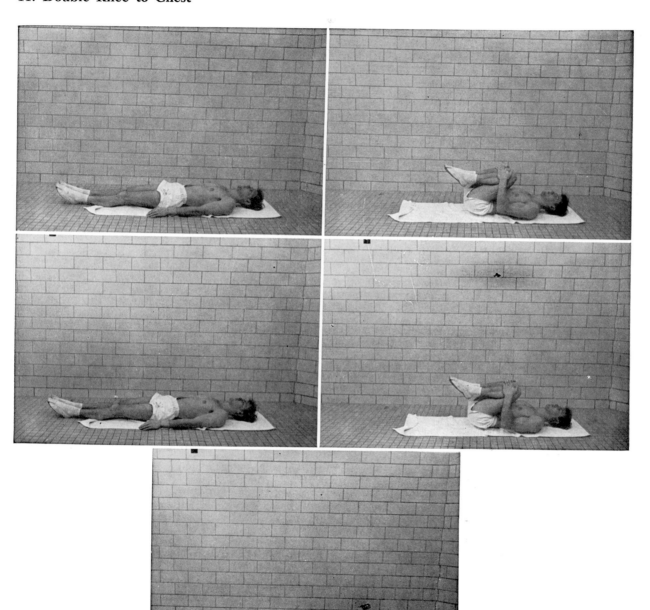

12. Rowing Exercise

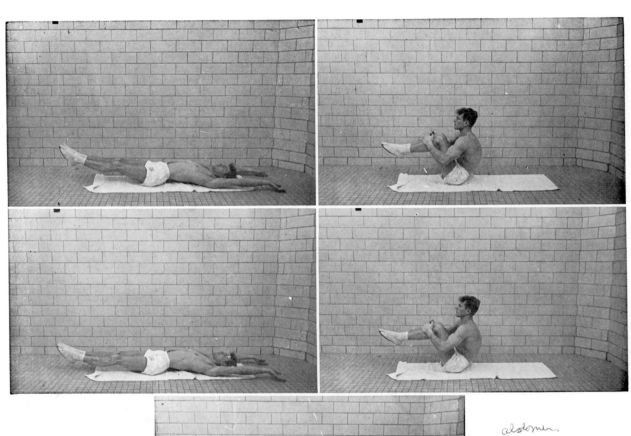

13. Hip Raiser

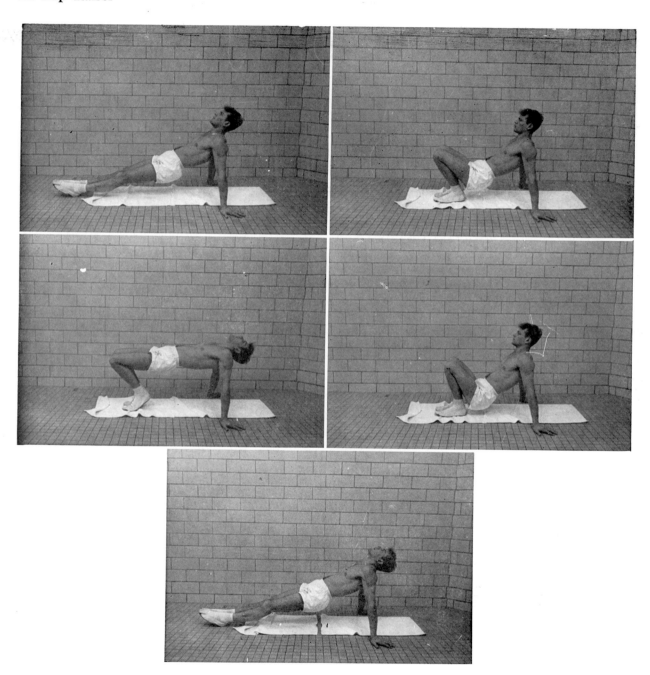

14. Back Shuffler from Back Leaning Rest Position

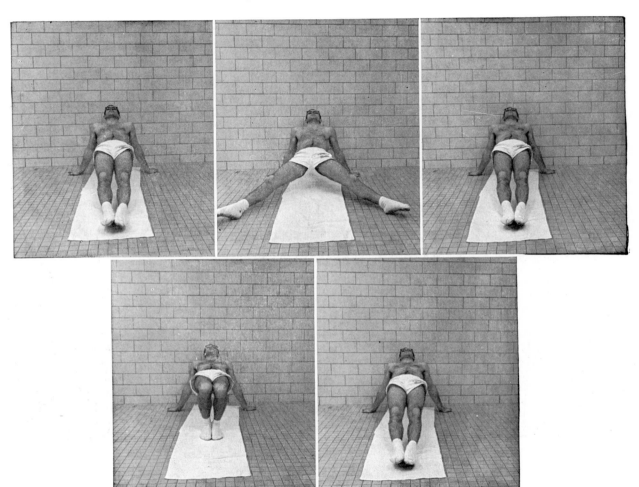

15. Leg Kick from Back Leaning Rest Position — Feet 18 inches Apart

16. Horizontal Running (Full Squat — Hands on the Ground)

17. Push-ups

18. Opposite Leg and Arm Raiser

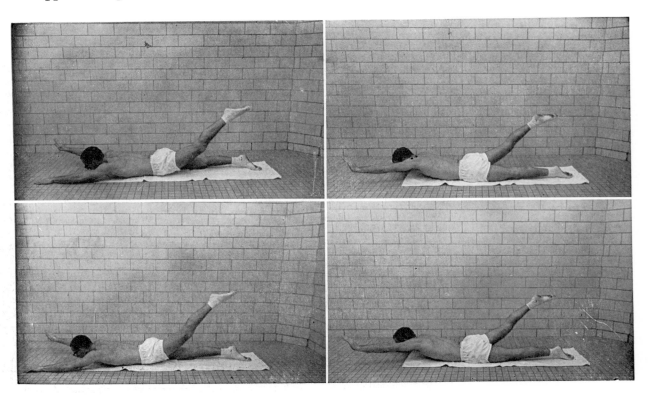

19. Leg Crossover from Back Lying Position

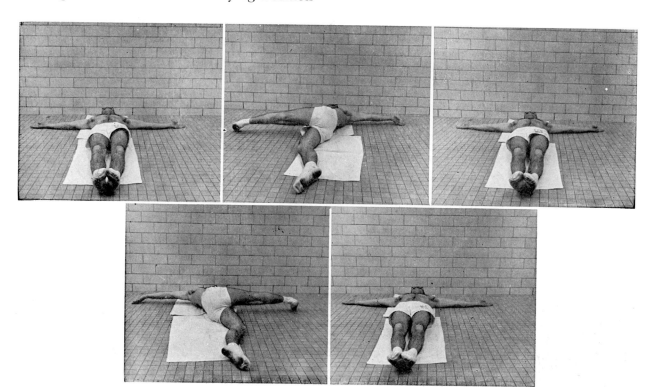

20. Leg Lift Side Lying — Exercise Both Legs

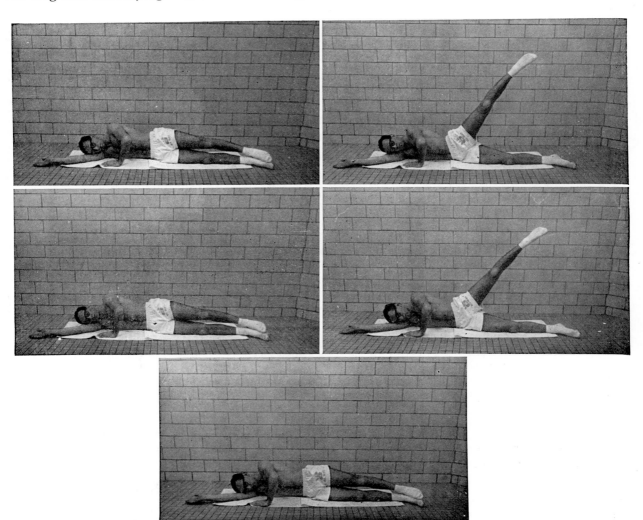

STRENGTHEN ALL WEAK AREAS

All weak areas in the body must be strengthened in the off-season and pre-season conditioning programs. The wrestler should have a prescribed exercise program for his individual needs in the off-season. In the pre-season the coach or trainer can give the wrestler a muscle strength test to be sure he has strengthened his weak area in the off-season.

Every wrestler has some areas in the body that are weak and need strengthening exercise. Wrestling is a strong man's sport with many muscle injuries. Weakness may be due to having some area in the body in which the wrestler has never developed enough strength. We know from research that any area that has been injured must be restrengthened before every season and must be kept strong by daily resistive exercise throughout the season.

When there is a muscle tear or a ligament tear, the body repairs this injury with scar tissue. Scar tissue never functions like normal tissue. It never has the same blood supply; it is not elastic as it was originally; and it does not have the same sensory nerve supply. We can redevelop the strength in the injured tissue, but if we do not do some resistive exercise daily to keep it strong throughout the season, the strength will drop off. Through disuse or sometimes even through normal wrestling activity and exercise, we may lose twenty to twenty-five pounds of strength as the season goes on. Without resistive exercise daily we usually reinjure the weak area or injure another area protecting the weak area.

Each individual wrestler must find out how much resistive exercise he needs to keep his weak muscles strong. Every injury is different, so perhaps you may find you need to do resistive exercise only twice a week to stay strong. Others may have to exercise daily to stay strong.

Find out how much exercise you need to keep your weak ankle, leg, back, shoulder, or arm strong; and keep exercising.

Wrestling coaches should not leave this decision to the individual wrestler during the regular season, as he may not do enough resistive exercise to keep his weak area strong.

Require all wrestlers on your team to work at least ten minutes a day on strength exercise. These exercises should be prescribed for each individual wrestler according to his weak area and strength needs. It is a good idea to make every wrestler work on increasing and maintaining his leg, ankle, and back strength daily. Most wrestlers will work on their upper body themselves without too much prodding. However, it may be necessary to require and prescribe exercises for the upper extremities, chest and upper back for some wrestlers.

The coach should not ask wrestlers to exercise and get strong — he should show them what to do and should count for them. He should mark the exercises in the book he wants each individual wrestler to do in the off-season while he is at home or away from school. In the pre-season and regular season the whole team should work together after practice for at least ten minutes a day on resistive strength exercise. The coach or trainer should prescribe the individual exercises for each wrestler and supervise to see that he does them correctly. Some coaches use weights. Others use the two-man isometric exercises as shown in the book, or Spackman Isometric Exercise Equipment. The coach can use any type of exercise he prefers, but should insist on exercise and should supervise the exercise program.

If the wrestler will strengthen all weak areas, he will have fewer injuries and more winning wrestling seasons.

ISOMETRIC EXERCISE PROCEDURE

1. One person does the exercise — a partner provides the resistance. Change positions. Your partner does the exercise while you resist. In the beginning do not try to exert full effort.

2. Each man repeats the exercise three times, resisting six seconds each time.

3. Push or pull as hard as you can without pain for six seconds; relax six seconds; push six seconds; relax six seconds; push six seconds; relax.

4. There should be little or no movement through a range of motion during the isometric exercise. Resist and maintain the correct angle during the exercise.

5. When resisting, do not try to push your partner down. Hold as though you were an immovable object maintaining the correct angle.

6. You should not experience pain during the exercise. Should you have any pain, ease off then push as hard as you can without pain. As strength increases the pain will leave. If pain continues, consult your physician before resuming any exercise.

7. Never push or pull so hard that you feel like you may black out. An individual can gain in strength pushing or pulling at 60 percent to 80 percent of his best effort.

8. Begin each contraction slowly and ease off the contraction slowly at the end of the six second contraction.

9. Exercise at least three different positions through a complete range of motion to strengthen the entire muscle — at 15 degrees, 45 degrees, 90 degrees, and perhaps at 135 degrees.

ISOMETRIC EXERCISE

Isometric exercise is a fast method of gaining and maintaining strength for the wrestler. Isometric exercise is not a cure-all to replace all other forms of exercise. Weights, cables, and wall pulleys may be better to strengthen some muscle groups. Some wrestlers prefer lifting weights. Whichever method is used to increase strength, the wrestler should be sure he is exercising correctly, or he may not strengthen the area. Isometric exercise is used in the book to show how to strengthen all areas of the body, since many schools do not have weights and wall pulleys.

No matter which type of exercise is preferred, the muscle must be exercised in the same way to strengthen a given area. In isometric exercise, a partner resists the movement at different points through a complete range of motion, or you can push against an immovable object. In weight training, the weight supplies the resistance in the same movement through a complete range of motion, lifting the weight slowly and returning slowly to the starting position. You may also lift the weight and stop at different points for six seconds through a range of motion. This is referred to as isotonic-isometric exercise. Exercise any way you prefer, but get strong for wrestling.

In the two-man isometric exercise program described in this book, you do not need any equipment, and you do not need as many repetitions. Three six-second contractions at different points along the complete range is enough to gain or maintain strength. In weak areas we suggest you work three times a day to increase your strength.

If you are strong in most areas of the body, you may not need to exercise the whole body isometrically. However, with a partner you both can strengthen the whole body in a thirty to forty-five-minute two-man isometric exercise session.

Should you have weak shoulders, you may only need to strengthen the shoulders, chest, and upper back. In an off-season or pre-season program, your coach or trainer should tell you what areas you need to strengthen (from your past injury record) or the areas he would like you to develop to improve your wrestling ability for the coming wrestling season. Using this book the coach can mark the exercises he wants each wrestler to do to be sure to strengthen his weak shoulder, knee, back, or any weak area. Each wrestler will have his own book and personal exercise program for his individual strength needs.

Before beginning your isometric exercise program, always spend at least ten minutes doing stretching and warm-up exercises. Choose the exercises carefully to strengthen your weak areas and the areas of the body that are most essential for wrestling. Find a fellow wrestler and go to work exercising for thirty to forty-five minutes. In the pre-season program, you'll probably work five days a week with at least ten minutes of isometric exercise for strength, along with your wrestling work on the mats. In the regular season continue working at least ten minutes on isometric strength exercise.

You should never have pain while doing isometric exercise. Should you have any pain, ease off the contraction and push or pull only as hard as you can without pain. You can gain and maintain strength by pushing or pulling with a 60 to 80 percent effort. Follow the exercise directions closely to be sure the exercises are done correctly in order to achieve the desired results. Should you prefer weight training over isometric exercise — use the same exercises and put weights in the hands, or on the feet, and lift the weights very slowly.

Neck Exercises

After engaging in selected stretching and warm-up exercises, we shall begin the two-man isometric exercises at the neck and work downward. Each exercise is given to exercise the prime movers, the major muscles that initiate the action in any movement. Follow the exercises closely to be sure they are done correctly in order to achieve the desired results (see isometric exercise procedure on page 58).

1. Neck Flexion

   a. Bring your chin towards your chest.

   b. Your partner attempts to push your head back, resisting for six seconds with his palm on your forehead.

   c. Your partner does the same exercise, bringing his head towards his chest.

   d. Resist for six seconds with your palm on his forehead.

   e. Each man repeats the exercise three times for a total of eighteen seconds exercise for each man.

2. Neck Extension

   a. Push your head back as far as possible.

   b. Your partner attempts to push your head forward, resisting for six seconds with his palm on the back of your head.

   c. Your partner does the same exercise pushing his head back as far as possible.

   d. Resist for six seconds with your palm on the back of his head.

   e. Each man repeats the exercise three times for a total of eighteen seconds exercise for each man.

3. Neck Lateral Flexion

   a. Push your head to the side, bringing your ear toward your shoulder.

   b. Your partner attempts to push your head back to a straight position, resisting for six seconds with his palm on the side of your head.

   c. Your partner does the same exercise pushing his head to the side bringing his ear towards his shoulder.

   d. Resist for six seconds with your palm on the side of his head.

   e. Repeat the exercise pushing your head toward the other shoulder.

   f. Each man repeats the exercise three times on each side for a total of thirty-six seconds of exercise for each man.

Shoulder and Arm Exercises

1. Shoulder Flexion (Lift Arms Forward)

a. Raise the arms forward to 90 degrees with the elbows straight and the palms down. Keep your stomach muscles tight and your back straight.

b. Your partner attempts to push your arms down toward the floor, resisting for six seconds with his palms on the back of your hand and wrist.

c. Your partner does the same exercise, bringing his arms forward to 90 degrees. Be sure not to lean backward. Keep your stomach muscles tight.

d. Resist for six seconds with your palm on the back of his hand and wrist.

e. Each man repeats the exercise three times.

f. Exercise at three different positions through a complete range of motion in shoulder flexion — 15 degrees, 45 degrees and at 90 degrees as shown in the picture.

2. Shoulder Abduction (Lift Arms Sideward)

a. Raise the arms sideward to 90 degrees with the elbows straight and the palms down. Keep your stomach muscles tight and your back straight.

b. Your partner attempts to push your arms

down toward the floor, resisting for six seconds with his palms on the back of your hand and wrist.

c. Your partner does the same exercise, raising his arms sideward to 90 degrees. Be sure not to lean backward. Keep your stomach muscles tight.

d. Resist for six seconds with your palm on the back of his hand and wrist.

e. Each man repeats the exercise three times.

f. Exercise at three different positions through a complete range of motion in shoulder abduction — 15 degrees, 45 degrees and at 90 degrees as shown in the picture.

3. Shoulder Horizontal Extension (Push Arms Backward)

a. With your back to your partner, raise the arms to 90 degrees, palms down. Push the arms backward, pinching the shoulder blades together. Keep the arms raised to 90 degrees and the stomach muscles tight.

b. Your partner attempts to push your arms forward, resisting for six seconds with his palms on the side of your hand and wrist.

c. Your partner does the same exercise pushing his arms backward, pinching his shoulder blades together. Be sure to keep the elbows straight, arms raised to 90 degrees and the stomach muscles tight.

d. Brace yourself with one foot forward, and do not lean backward while exercising.

e. Resist for six seconds with your palms on the side of his hand and wrist.

f. Each man repeats the exercise three times.

g. Exercise at three different positions through complete range of motion in shoulder horizontal extension 15 degrees, arms in front of the body 45 degrees and at 90 degrees as shown in the picture.

NOTE:

1. All shoulder exercises except numbers 4, 7 and 8 can be done sitting in a chair facing your partner.

2. When working with two people or in small groups, better stabilization can be maintained while sitting in a chair.

4. Shoulder Shrug

a. With your back to your partner, raise your shoulders as high as possible, bringing your shoulders toward your ears with your elbows bent.

b. Your partner hangs all of his body weight on your shoulders and attempts to pull your shoulders down, resisting for six seconds.

c. Your partner does the same exercise, hanging his body weight on your shoulders. You may have to lean forward a little to keep your balance.

d. Resist for six seconds with your body weight hanging on his shoulders.

e. Each man repeats the exercise three times.

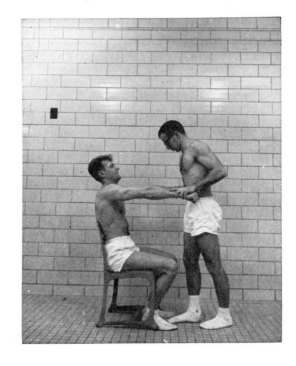

3. When working with athletic teams or large groups, the exercises may be done standing, with special emphasis on keeping the abdominal muscles tight and standing up straight.
4. Exercise at three different positions through a complete range of motion — 15 degrees, 45 degrees and at 90 degrees as shown in the pictures.

5. Shoulder Elevation Sideward

a. Raise the arms sideward and backward to an overhead position to about 135 degrees, keeping the elbows straight and the palms facing forward.
b. Your partner attempts to pull your arms downward toward the floor, resisting for six seconds with his palms on the thumb and wrist.
c. Your partner does the same exercise, raising his arms sideward and backward to an overhead position to about 135 degrees. Keep your elbows straight and do not lean backward.
d. Resist for six seconds with your palms on the thumb and wrist.
e. Each man repeats the exercise three times.

6. Shoulder External Rotation

a. Raise the arms sideward to 90 degrees, and bend the elbows to 90 degrees with the palms

forward.
b. Rotate your shoulders outward.
c. Your partner attempts to rotate your shoulders forward by grasping your wrists, resisting for six seconds.
d. Your partner does the same exercise raising his arms sideward to 90 degrees and bending his elbows to 90 degrees. Keep your stomach muscles tight.
e. Resist for six seconds by grasping his wrists and attempting to rotate his shoulders internally.
f. Each man repeats the exercise three times.
g. Exercise at three different positions through a complete range of motion in shoulder external rotation — 45 degrees, 90 degrees, as shown in the picture and at complete external rotation.

7. Shoulder Internal Rotation

a. Raise the arms sideward to 90 degrees and bend the elbows to 90 degrees with the palms forward.
b. Rotate your shoulders internally. Keep your stomach muscles tight.
c. Your partner attempts to push your shoulders externally by grasping your wrists, resisting for six seconds.
d. Your partner does the same exercise, raising

his arms sideward to 90 degrees and bending his elbows to 90 degrees. Keep your stomach muscles tight.

e. Resist for six seconds by grasping his wrists and attempting to rotate his shoulders externally.

f. Each man repeats the exercise three times.

g. Exercise at three different positions through a complete range of motion in shoulder internal rotation — complete external rotation, 90 degrees as shown in the picture, and at 45 degrees.

NOTE:

Exercises 6 and 7 may also be done lying on the back for better stabilization. See pictures for illustration. Raise the arms sideward to 90 degrees and bend the elbows to 90 degrees with

8. Shoulder Scapular Abduction

a. Raise the arms forward to 90 degrees with the palms up facing your partner. Push your arms forward reaching as far as possible while keeping your stomach muscles tight. Step forward with one foot for stabilization.

b. Your partner grasps your hands and attempts to push your arms backward and your shoulder blades together, resisting for six seconds.

c. Your partner does the same exercise raising his arms forward to 90 degrees and his palms up facing his partner.

d. Resist for six seconds by grasping his hands and attempting to push his arms backward and his shoulder blades together.

e. Each man repeats the exercise three times.

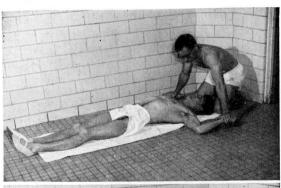

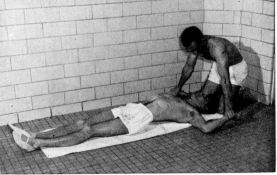

the palms up. Attempt to rotate the shoulders externally as your partner resists for six seconds. Attempt to rotate the shoulders internally as your partner resists for six seconds. Each man repeats the exercise three times. Exercise at three different positions through a complete range of motion in internal and external rotation.

9. Shoulder Scapular Abduction

a. Lying on your back, push your arms toward the ceiling, stretching as far as possible and keeping your elbows straight.

b. Your partner, with his body held rigid, balances his hips on your hands. Attempt to hold all of his body weight, resisting for six seconds.

c. Your partner does the same exercise, pushing his arms toward the ceiling and attempting to hold all of your body weight.

d. Resist for six seconds.

e. Each man repeats the exercise three times.

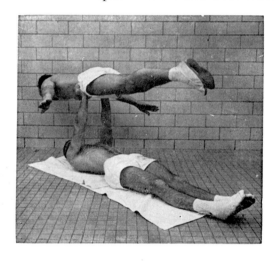

10. Elbow Flexion

a. Bend your elbows to 90 degrees bringing the palms toward your shoulders. Keep your stomach muscles tight. Bend the knees slightly for balance.

b. Your partner grasps your hands and attempts to straighten your elbows, resisting for six seconds.

c. Your partner does the same exercise bending his elbows to 90 degrees with the palms up.

d. Resist for six seconds, attempting to straighten his elbows.

e. Each man repeats the exercise three times.

f. Exercise at three different positions through a complete range of motion in flexion — 15 degrees, 90 degrees as shown in the picture, and at 135 degrees.

NOTE:

Exercise 10 should also be done by bringing the thumb toward the shoulder and by bringing the back of the hand toward the shoulder. Resistance is given the same way. Each man repeats the exercise three times each way. Exercise at three different positions through a complete range of motion in elbow flexion.

11. Elbow Extension

a. With your back to your partner, raise your arms directly overhead with the elbows bent slightly behind your head.

b. Bend your knees slightly for balance. Keep your stomach muscles tight.

c. Your partner grasps your wrists and attempts to prevent you from straightening your elbows, resisting for six seconds.

d. Your partner does the same exercise, raising his arms directly overhead with the elbows slightly bent.

e. Resist for six seconds to prevent him from straightening his elbows.

f. Each man repeats the exercise three times.

g. Exercise at three different positions through a complete range of motion in elbow extension — 135 degrees, 90 degrees, as shown in the picture, and at 15 degrees.

Wrist Exercises

1. Wrist Extension

a. Sit facing your partner with your forearms resting on your thighs for stabilization, the back of your hands up toward the ceiling, wrists held down just beyond your knees.

b. Partner sitting facing you attempts to push your hands down while you resist for six seconds.

c. Partner sits with the backs of his hands toward the ceiling.

d. You attempt to push his hands down while he resists for six seconds.

e. Each man repeats the exercise three times.

2. Wrist Flexion

a. Sit facing your partner with your forearms resting on your thighs, with the palm of your hands up toward the ceiling, wrists held down just beyond your knees.

b. Partner sitting facing you attempts to push your hands down while you resist for six seconds.

c. Partner sits with the backs of his hands toward the ceiling.

d. You attempt to push his hands down while he resists for six seconds.

e. Each man repeats the exercise three times.

3. Wrist Abduction

a. Sit facing your partner with your forearms resting on your thighs, with the thumbs toward the ceiling, wrists held straight just beyond your knees.

b. Partner sitting facing you attempts to push your hands down while you resist for six seconds.

c. Partner sits with the thumbs toward the ceiling.

d. You attempt to push his hands down while he resists for six seconds.

e. Each man repeats the exercise three times.

4. Wrist Adduction

a. Sit facing your partner with your forearms resting on your thighs, with the thumbs

toward the ceiling, wrists held straight just beyond your knees.

b. Partner sits facing you and attempts to push your hands up toward the ceiling while you resist for six seconds.

c. Partner sits with the thumbs toward the ceiling.

d. You attempt to push his hands upward while he resists for six seconds.

e. Each man repeats the exercise three times.

NOTE:

The four wrist exercises can be given without a partner by providing your own resistance with each hand. Repeat each exercise three times with six-second contractions and six seconds of rest between each exercise.

5. Wrist Pronation (Turning Palms Down)

a. Sit facing your partner. Extend your arms with the palms up.

b. Partner sitting facing you crosses his hands and grips your hands resisting you for six seconds. You try to turn your hands over to see the back of your hands.

c. Partner sits with his palms toward the ceiling.

d. Cross your hands and grip his hands. Resist his turning his hands over for six seconds.

e. Each man repeats the exercise three times.

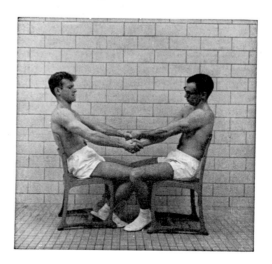

6. Wrist Supination (Turning Palms Up)

   a. Sit facing your partner. Extend your arms with the palms down.
   b. Partner sitting facing you crosses his hands and grips your hands. You attempt to turn your hands over to bring your palms up; partner resists for six seconds.
   c. Partner sits with the back of his hands toward the ceiling.
   d. Cross your hands and grip his hands. Resist his turning the palms up for six seconds.
   e. Each man repeats the exercise three times.

Finger and Hand Exercise

Strongs hands are a must for the wrestler. Wrestling with teammates will not give you strong hands with strength you can maintain throughout the long season.

Once the first day of practice begins, the wrestler always has a weak, bruised hand, a jammed thumb or finger, or a sprained wrist. He must do something in the off-season and pre-season to strengthen his hands and fingers. He will do the same exercises daily during the regular season to keep his hands strong or to restrengthen his jammed fingers or injured wrist and hand. The hand and fingers are always suffering from contusions from hitting the mats hard, hyperextending the fingers and thumb when an opponent pulls on your fingers to break a hold, or jamming the fingers and thumb into an opponent in attempting a take down.

There are many hand exercises on the market, but one of the best hand exercisers is the Ed Block Hand Exerciser.*

The wrestling team should have an Ed Block Hand Exerciser and should carry it wherever it goes. Coaches, if budgets permit, should supply a hand exerciser for each wrestler to keep in his locker. This way the wrestlers will exercise their hands every day and increase their hand and finger strength (see the pictures below).

---

*Available from Skill Surgical, Inc., 5406 Hartford Road, Baltimore, Maryland 21214, for $2.00.

The Ed Block Hand Exerciser is one of the few exercisers with which you can strengthen the extensor muscles of the fingers and wrist. By digging the fingers in the putty and extending each finger you can strengthen the extensor muscles of each finger. To have a strong wrist and hand you must strengthen both the flexors and extensors of the fingers and wrist.

Squeezing a ball will help, but it will only get you strong in one area, depending on the size of the ball. You cannot strengthen the fingers through a complete range of motion in finger flexion, and you cannot strengthen the extensors of the fingers and wrist with a rubber ball.

The following hand and finger exercises should be done daily by the wrestler with the Ed Block Hand Exerciser.

1. A Word of Caution

a. Do not use the Ed Block Hand Exercises following a serious hand injury or fracture unless prescribed by your physician.
b. This is a strenuous exercise program; stop exercising when your muscles become fatigued.
c. Like all exercise programs, begin with just a few exercises on the first few days.
d. You will get some muscle soreness in the fingers, wrists and forearms.

2. Procedure for the Whole Hand

a. Hold the putty in one hand.
b. Squeeze the putty with the whole hand; hold it tightly for six seconds; relax.
c. Squeeze the putty in the other hand; hold it tightly for six seconds; relax.
d. Squeeze the putty three times in each hand.

3. Procedure for the Individual Fingers (Finger Flexors)

a. Hold the putty in one hand.
b. Squeeze the putty between the tips of the index finger and the thumb; squeeze tightly for six seconds; relax.
c. Squeeze the putty between the tips of the middle finger and the thumb; squeeze tightly for six seconds; relax.
d. Repeat the exercise using each finger and thumb, holding for six seconds.
e. Exercise the other hand following the same procedure.

4. Procedure for the Individual Fingers (Finger Extensors)

a. Hold the putty in the palm of the hand.
b. Dig the fingernails and tips of the fingers into the putty.
c. Slowly try to straighten the fingers, one finger at a time, pushing against the putty.
d. Repeat the exercise three times with each finger.
e. Exercise the other hand following the same procedure.

5. Continuing Procedure

a. Carry your exerciser with you.
b. Exercise only once a day for the first few days.
c. After the initial muscle soreness subsides, you may exercise as often as you like to increase your hand, finger and wrist strength.
d. Strong hands are a must in all sports.

Chest Exercises

1. Pull Your Arms Straight Across Your Chest (Back Lying)

a. Raise your arms out to the side to 90 degrees with your elbows straight and your palms up.
b. Your partner grasps your wrists and attempts to hold the backs of your hands to the ground or floor as you lift your arms to go across your chest, resisting for six seconds. Keep your elbows straight.
c. Your partner does the same exercise lifting his arms to go across his chest as you attempt to hold the backs of his hands to the ground or floor, resisting for six seconds.
d. Each man repeats the exercise three times.
e. Exercise at three different positions through a complete range of motion — at 15 de-

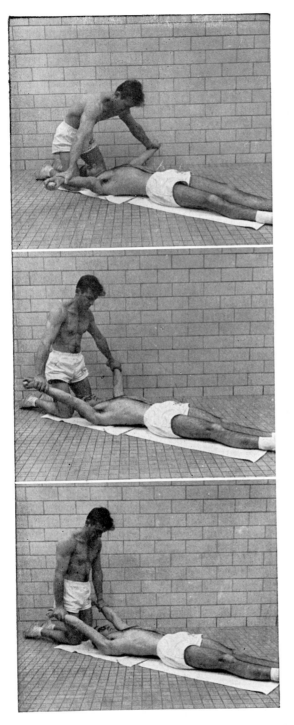

grees, 45 degrees, as shown in the picture, and at 90 degrees, with the arms perpendicular to the chest.

2. Pull Your Arms Towards Your Opposite Hip (Back Lying)

a. Raise your arms overhead to a 45 degree angle with your elbows straight, palms up and the backs of the hands on the ground or floor.

b. Your partner grasps your wrists and attempts to hold the backs of your hands on the ground or floor as you pull across your chest toward your opposite hip, resisting for six seconds.

c. Your partner does the same exercise lifting his arms to go across his chest toward his opposite hip, resisting for six seconds.

d. Each man repeats the exercise three times.

e. Exercise at three different positions through a complete range of motion — at 15 degrees, 45 degrees, as shown in the picture, and at 90 degrees, with the arms perpendicular to the chest.

3. Pull Your Arms Straight Down Towards Your Hips (Back Lying)

a. Raise your arms directly overhead with your elbows straight, palms up and the backs of the hands on the ground or floor.

b. Your partner grasps your wrists and attempts to hold the backs of your hands to the ground as you lift your arms to go down to your sides, resisting for six seconds. Keep your elbows straight.

c. Your partner does the same exercise lifting his arms to bring them up and to his sides, resisting for six seconds.

d. Each man repeats the exercise three times.

e. Exercise at three different positions through a complete range of motion at 15 degrees, 45 degrees, as shown in the picture, and at 90 degrees, with the arms perpendicular to the chest.

Abdominal Exercises

1. V Sit-up (Back Lying)

a. Raise both legs and your upper body simultaneously, keeping your legs straight with arms out straight for balance.

b. Your partner attempts to push your back and legs to the ground, resisting for six seconds.

c. Your partner does the same exercise lifting the upper body and the legs. Your arms are raised in front of your body for balance.

d. Resist for six seconds.

e. Each man repeats the exercise three times.

2. Bent Knees Sit-up (Back Lying)

a. Raise the upper body off the ground in a half sit-up position with the hips and knees bent, feet on the ground near your buttocks, fingers laced behind your head.

b. Your partner sits on your feet and holds your knees for stabilization while pushing on your chest or elbows, resisting for six seconds.

c. At the end of the six-second contraction, continue the sit-up, touching the chest to the knees. Slowly return to the back lying position.

d. Your partner does the same exercise while you attempt to push him back towards the ground, resisting for six seconds. Continue the sit-up, touching the chest to the knees. Slowly return to the starting position.

e. Each man repeats the exercise three times.

3. Straight Leg Sit-up

a. Raise the upper body off the ground in a half sit-up position with the legs out straight, fingers laced behind your head.

b. Your partner sits on your legs for stabilization while pushing on your chest or elbows, attempting to push your back towards the ground, resisting for six seconds.

c. At the end of the six-second contraction, continue the sit-up, touching the elbows to the knees. Slowly return to the back-lying position.

d. Your partner does the same exercise while you attempt to push his back toward the ground, resisting for six seconds. Continue the sit-up, touching the chest to the knees. Slowly return to the starting position.

e. Each man repeats the exercise three times.

4. Lateral Sit-up (Side Lying)

a. Lie on your right side with your right arm across your chest. The left arm is raised to the side for balance.

b. Your partner sits straddling your thighs for stabilization.

c. Raise the upper body off the floor laterally as high as possible.

d. Your partner attempts to push you down toward the ground with his hand on the side of your chest, resisting for six seconds.

e. Your partner does the same exercise while you attempt to push his upper body to the ground, resisting for six seconds.

f. Each man repeats the exercise on each side three times.

Back Exercises

1. Shoulder Hyperextension

a. Face lying, raise your arms as high as possible with the elbows straight and your palms up.

b. Your partner sits straddling your thighs.

c. Your partner attempts to push your arms to the ground, resisting for six seconds.

d. Your partner does the same exercise while you attempt to push his arms down, resisting for six seconds.

e. Each man repeats the exercise three times.

f. Exercise at three different positions through a complete range of motion in shoulder hyperextension — at 15 degrees, as shown in the picture, 45 degrees and at complete shoulder hyperextension.

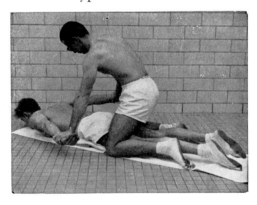

2. Shoulder Hyperextention (Shoulder Blade Pinched)

a. Face lying, pinch your shoulder blades together tightly and raise your arms as high as possible with the elbows straight and your palms up.

b. Your partner sits straddling your thighs.

c. Your partner attempts to push your arms to the ground, resisting for six seconds. Keep your shoulder blades pinched tightly.

d. Your partner does the same exercise while you attempt to push his arms down, resisting for six seconds.

e. Each man repeats the exercise three times.

f. Exercise at three different positions through a complete range of motion in shoulder hyperextension — at 15 degrees, as shown in the picture, 45 degrees and at complete range of motion in shoulder hyperextension.

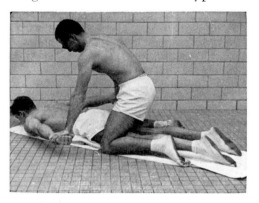

3. Scapular Adduction (Lift Arms Toward the Ceiling)

a. Face lying, raise the arms out to the side to 90 degrees. Rotate the arms externally with the thumb pointing upward toward the ceiling.

b. Your partner sits straddling your low back or kneeling beside your body.

c. Raise your arms as high as possible, leading with your thumbs while pinching your shoulder blades together.

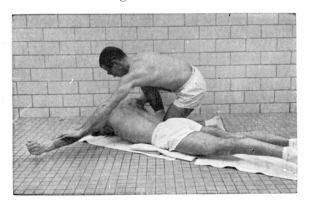

d. Your partner attempts to push your arms down with his palm on your wrists, resisting for six seconds.

e. Your partner does the same exercise while you attempt to push his arms down, resisting for six seconds.

f. Each man repeats the exercise three times.

g. Exercise at three different positions through a complete range of motion in scapular adduction.

4. Shoulder Flexion

a. Face lying, raise the arms overhead to an angle of 45 degrees with your elbows straight and the back of your hands towards the ceiling.

b. Your partner is kneeling in front, near your head.

c. Raise your arms with the elbows straight and off the ground as high as possible while keeping your forehead on the ground.

d. Your partner attempts to push your arms down with his palms on the back of your hands and wrists, resisting for six seconds.

e. Your partner does the same exercise while you attempt to push his arms down, resisting for six seconds.

f. Each man repeats the exercise three times.

g. Exercise at three different positions through a complete range of motion in shoulder flexion.

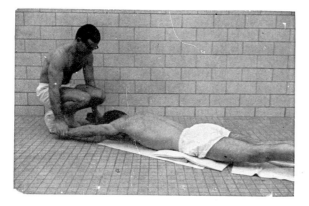

5. Back Hyperextension

a. Face lying, raise the head and chest off the ground as high as possible with the fingers laced behind your head.

b. Your partner sits straddling your thighs for stabilization.

c. Your partner attempts to push your chest toward the ground, resisting for six seconds.

d. Your partner does the same exercise while you attempt to push his chest toward the ground, resisting for six seconds.

e. Each man repeats the exercise three times.

f. Exercise at three different positions through a complete range of motion in back hyperextension.

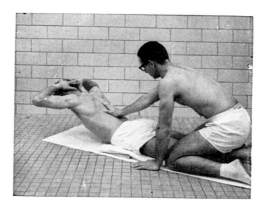

6. Thigh Extension (Straight Leg Raising)

a. Face lying with the arms at the side of the body with the palms up.

b. Raise the leg off the ground just clearing the kneecap off the ground. Keep the knee straight and both hips on the ground.

c. Your partner is kneeling by your legs.

d. Your partner attempts to push your straight leg toward the ground, resisting for six seconds.

e. Your partner does the same exercise while you attempt to push his leg toward the ground, resisting for six seconds.

f. Each man repeats the exercise three times with each leg.

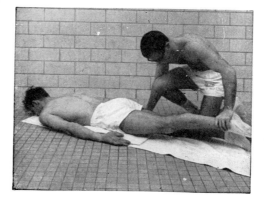

7. Thigh Extension (Straight Leg Raising)

a. Face lying with the arms at the side of the body with the palms up.
b. Raise the leg off the ground as high as possible, keeping the knee straight and both hips on the ground.
c. Your partner is kneeling by your legs.
d. Your partner attempts to push your straight leg toward the ground, resisting for six seconds.
e. Your partner does the same exercise while you attempt to push his leg toward the ground, resisting for six seconds.
f. Each man repeats the exercise three times with each leg.

8. Thigh Extension (Bent Knee Leg Raising)

a. Face lying with the arms at the side of the body with the palms up.
b. Bend one knee and lift the bent knee off the ground as high as possible, keeping both hips on the ground.
c. Your partner is kneeling by your legs.
d. Your partner attempts to push your thigh toward the ground, resisting for six seconds.
e. Your partner does the same exercise while you attempt to push his thigh toward the ground, resisting for six seconds.
f. Each man repeats the exercise three times with each leg.

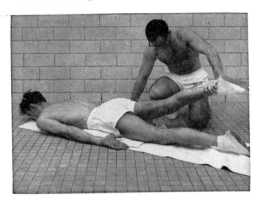

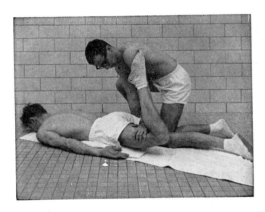

Hip Exercises

1. Hip Abduction (Sideward Leg Raising)

a. Side lying, the lower leg is bent for stabilization. The top leg is held with the knee straight. Raise the straight leg as high as possible, rotating the leg inward so that you lead with your heel.

b. Your partner is kneeling by your hips.
c. Your partner attempts to push your leg down giving resistance at the knee for six seconds.
d. Your partner does the same exercise as you resist at the knee for six seconds.
e. Each man repeats the exercise three times with each leg.
f. Exercise at three different positions through a complete range of motion in hip abduction.

2. Hip Abduction (Sideward Leg Raising)

a. Side lying, the lower leg is bent for stabilization. The top leg is held with the knee straight. The top leg is bent (flexed) at the hip to an angle of 45 degrees, keeping the knee straight.
b. Raise the top leg as high as possible, rotating the leg inward so that you lead with the heel.
c. Your partner is kneeling by your hip.
d. Your partner attempts to push your leg down

giving resistance at the knee for six seconds.

e. Your partner does the same exercise as you resist at the knee for six seconds.

f. Each man repeats the exercise three times with each leg.

g. Exercise at three different positions through a complete range of motion in hip abduction.

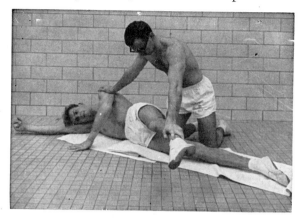

3. Hip Flexion (Straight Leg Raising)

a. Back lying, raise the leg about 3 inches off the ground at the heel with the knee held straight. Your arms are held at the side.

b. Your partner is kneeling by your hips.

c. Your partner attempts to push your leg down, giving resistance at the ankle for six seconds.

d. Repeat the exercise with the other leg.

e. Your partner does the same exercise as you resist at the ankle for six seconds.

f. Each man repeats the exercise three times with each leg.

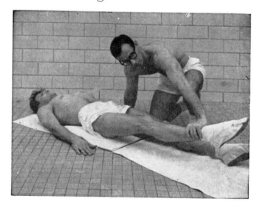

4. Hip Flexion (Straight Leg Raising)

a. Back lying, raise the leg to 15 degrees with the knee held straight. Your arms are held at the side. Your partner is kneeling by your hips.

b. Your partner attempts to push your leg down giving resistance at the ankle for six seconds.

c. Repeat the exercise with the other leg.

d. Your partner does the same exercise as you resist at the ankle for six seconds.

e. Each man repeats the exercise three times with each leg.

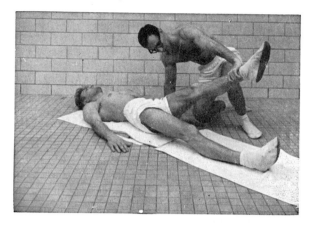

5. Hip Flexion (Knee Bent)

a. Sit on a table with the knees bent (flexed) to 90 degrees. A towel is rolled under the knees for comfort. The hands are on the

outside of the knees, holding the table for stabilization.

b. Your partner is standing in front of your legs.

c. Raise your knee toward the ceiling keeping your knee bent.

d. Your partner attempts to push your leg down, giving resistance at the top of the knee for six seconds.

e. Repeat the exercise with the other leg.

f. Your partner does the same exercise as you resist at the knee for six seconds.

g. Each man repeats the exercise three times with each leg.

h. Exercise at three different positions through a complete range of motion in hip flexion.

6. Hip Flexion, Hip External Rotation and Knee Flexion

a. Sit on a table with the knees bent (flexed) to 90 degrees. A towel is rolled under the knees for comfort. The hands are on the outside of the knees, holding the table for stabilization.

b. Your partner is standing in front of your legs.

c. Raise your leg, attempting to cross your leg, rotating the hip externally and bringing the heel up along the shin of your opposite leg.

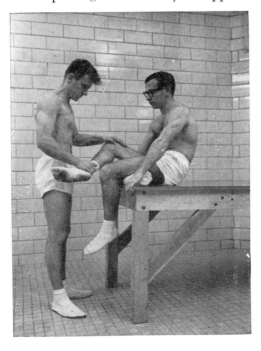

d. Your partner attempts to push your leg down, giving resistance with one hand on the top of your knee and the other hand grasping the ankle attempting to straighten your knee, resisting for six seconds.

e. Repeat the exercise with the other leg.

f. Your partner does the same exercise as you resist at the knee and ankle for six seconds.

g. Each man repeats the exercise three times with each leg.

h. Exercise at three different positions through a complete range of motion.

7. Hip Adduction (Hips and Knees Bent)

a. Back lying, your hips and knees are bent, (flexed) with the feet flat on the floor near your buttocks. Your arms are at the side of the body.

b. Your partner is kneeling by your hips.

c. Pull your knees together.

d. Your partner attempts to push your legs apart, giving resistance with one elbow wrapped around one knee and the other hand with the elbow straight against your other knee, resisting for six seconds.

e. Repeat the exercise three times, resting for six seconds between each exercise.

f. Your partner does the same exercise as you resist at the knees for six seconds.

g. Each man repeats the exercise three times.

h. Exercise at three different posititions through a complete range of motion.

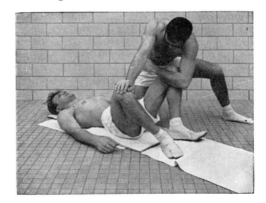

8. Hip Adduction (Hips and Knees Straight)

a. Back lying, your legs are out straight and spread apart to about 45 degrees with your arms at the side.

b. Your partner is kneeling between your knees with his knees against the inside of your knees. *Do not resist at the ankles.*

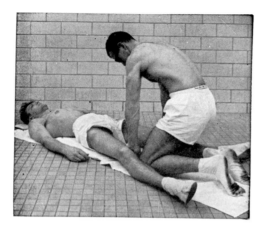

c. Pull your legs together.

d. Your partner stops you from bringing your legs together, giving resistance with his knees for six seconds.

e. Repeat the exercise three times, resting for six seconds between each exercise.

f. Your partner does the same exercise as you resist between the knees for six seconds.

g. Each man repeats the exercise three times.

NOTE:

Exercise number 8 should also be given with the legs spread about 3 in. and also spread about 6 in. to 8 in. apart at the knees. Resistance can be given with your two fists between your partner's knees. *Do not give resistance at the ankle as this will stretch the ligaments in the knee.*

Knee Exercises

1. Knee Extension

a. Sit on a table with the knees bent (flexed) over the edge of the table to 90 degrees. A towel is rolled under the knees for comfort. The hands are on the outside of the knees holding the table for stabilization.

b. Your partner is squatting in front of your legs. One hand is placed on the ankle, and the other hand is holding the leg of the table for stabilization.

c. Your partner holds your leg at 90 degrees while you attempt to extend your knee, resisting for six seconds.

d. Do not raise the buttocks or thigh off of the table during the exercise.

e. Repeat the exercises three times, resting for six seconds between each exercise.

f. Repeat the exercise three times with the other leg, or alternate exercising one leg and then the other leg.

g. Your partner does the same exercise as you resist at the ankle for six seconds.

h. Each man repeats the exercise three times with each leg.

2. Knee Extension

a. Sit on a table with the knee bent (flexed) over the edge of the table to 90 degrees. A towel is rolled under the knees for comfort. The hands are on the outside of the knees holding the table for stabilization.

b. Your partner is standing in front of your legs.

c. Raise one leg to 135 degrees.

d. Your partner attempts to push your leg down giving resistance at the ankle, for six seconds.

e. Do not raise buttocks or thighs off of the table during the exercise.

f. Repeat the exercise three times, resting for six seconds between each exercise.

g. Repeat the exercise three times with the other leg, or alternate exercising one leg and then the other leg.

h. Your partner does the same exercise as you resist at the ankle for six seconds.

i. Each man repeats the exercise three times with each leg.

3. Knee Extension

a. Sit on a table with the knees bent (flexed) over the edge of the table to 90 degrees. A towel is rolled under the knees for comfort. The hands are on the outside of the knees holding the table for stabilization.

b. Your partner is standing in front of your legs.

c. Straighten your knee to about 165 degrees, 15 degrees off complete knee extension.

d. Your partner attempts to push your leg down giving resistance at the ankle for six seconds.

e. Do not raise the buttocks or thigh off the table during the exercise.

f. Repeat the exercise three times, resting for six seconds between each exercise.

g. Repeat the exercise three times with the other leg, or alternate exercising one leg and then the other leg.

h. Your partner does the same exercise as you resist at the ankle for six seconds.

i. Each man repeats the exercise three times with each leg.

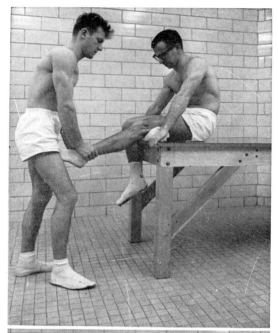

4. Knee Flexion

a. Face lying, the arms are along the side of the body with the palms up, the legs out straight. Your partner is kneeling by your legs.

b. Bend one knee until your shin is about 3 in. off the ground or the floor. Keep both hips and both shoulders on the floor or the ground.

c. Your partner attempts to push your leg down, giving resistance at the ankle for six seconds.

d. Keep both hips and both shoulders on the floor during the exercise.

e. Repeat the exercise three times, resting six seconds between each exercise.

f. Repeat the exercise three times with the other leg, or alternate exercising one leg and then the other leg.

g. Your partner does the same exercise as you resist at the ankle for six seconds.

h. Each man repeats the exercise three times with each leg.

5. Knee Flexion

a. Face lying, the arms are along the side of the body with the palms up, the legs are out

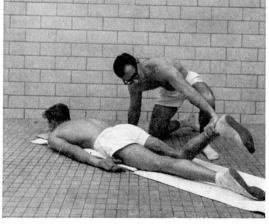

straight. Your partner is kneeling by your legs.

b. Bend one knee 135 degrees.

c. Your partner attempts to push your leg down, giving resistance at the ankle for six seconds.

d. Keep both hips and both shoulders on the floor during the exercise.

e. Repeat the exercise three times, resting six seconds between each exercise. Repeat the exercise three times with the other leg, or alternate exercising one leg and then the other leg.

f. Your partner does the same exercise as you resist at the ankle for six seconds.

g. Each man repeats the exercise three times with each leg.

Ankle Exercises

1. Ankle Inversion (Foot Turned In and Up)

a. Sit on a table with the knees bent (flexed) over the edge of the table to 90 degrees. A towel is rolled under the knees for comfort. The hands resting across the thighs.

b. Your partner is standing in front of your legs.

c. Raise your right leg to about 135 degrees. Push the foot down as far as possible.

d. Your partner places his left hand on the back of your right heel for stabilization. The right hand is placed on the inside of the right foot by the big toe.

e. Attempt to pull your right foot in and up, turning the sole of the foot to the inside. Your partner resists the attempt to pull your foot in and up for six seconds.

f. Repeat the exercise three times, resting six seconds between each exercise.

g. Repeat the exercise three times with the left ankle.

h. Reverse your hands for the left ankle with resistance given with the left hand.

i. Your partner does the same exercise as you resist at the ankle for six seconds.

j. Each man repeats the exercise three times with each ankle.

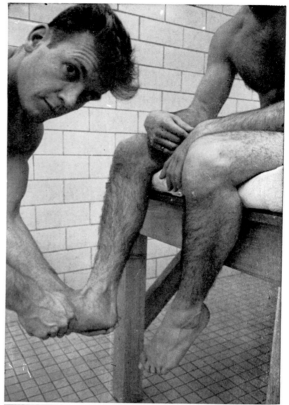

2. Ankle Dorsi-Flexion (Foot Pulled Straight Up)

a. Sit on a table with the knees bent (flexed) over the edge of the table to 90 degrees. A towel is rolled under the knees for comfort. The hands are resting across the thighs.

b. Your partner is standing in front of your legs.

c. Raise your right leg to about 135 degrees. Push the foot down as far as possible.

d. Your partner places his left hand on the back of your right heel for stabilization. The right hand is placed on the top of the foot and toes.

e. Attempt to pull your right foot straight upward toward your face. Your partner resists the attempt to pull your right foot straight up for six seconds.

f. Repeat the exercise three times, resting for six seconds between each exercise.

g. Repeat the exercise three times with the left ankle.

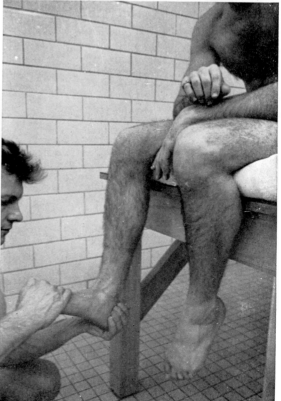

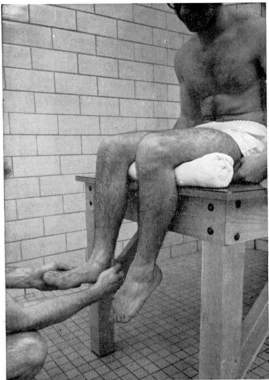

h. Reverse your hands for the left ankle with resistance given with the left hand.

i. Your partner does the same exercise as you resist at the ankle for six seconds.

j. Each man repeats the exercise three times with each ankle.

3. Ankle Eversion (Foot Turned Out and Up)

a. Sit on a table with the knees bent (flexed) over the edge of the table to 90 degrees. A towel is rolled under the knees for comfort.

b. Your partner is standing in front of your legs.

c. Raise your right leg to about 135 degrees. Push the foot down as far as posssible.

d. Your partner places his right hand on the back of your right heel for stabilization. The left hand is placed on the outside of the right foot by the little toe.

e. Attempt to pull your right foot out and up turning the sole of the foot to the outside. Your partner resists the attempt to pull your right foot out and up for six seconds.

f. Repeat the exercise three times, resting six seconds between each exercise.

g. Repeat the exercise three times with the left ankle.

h. Reverse your hands for the left ankle with resistance given with the right hand.

i. Your partner does the same exercise as you resist at the ankle for six seconds.

j. Each man repeats the exercise three times with each ankle.

4. Ankle Plantar-flexion (Rise on the Toes)

a. Stand with your back to your partner, with your feet 15 in. apart. Rise on your toes as high as possible keeping your back straight. Put your hands against the wall for stabilization.

b. Your partner hangs his body weight on your shoulders, if possible, attempting to force your heels to the ground, resisting for six seconds.

c. Your partner does the same exercise as you resist by hanging your body weight on his shoulders, resisting for six seconds.

d. Each man repeats the exercise three times.

e. When beginning this exercise your partner may not be able to take all of your weight. Begin with only one part of your weight and gradually add more weight.

NOTE:

Exercise 4 should also be done on one leg at a time. As your strength increases, add more weight.

5. Ankle Plantar-flexion (Rise on the Toes with the Knees Bent)

a. Stand with your back to your partner, with your feet about 15 in. apart. Do a half knee bend and rise on your toes as high as possible, keeping your back straight.

b. Keep your knees in a half knee bend position as you rise on your toes.

c. Your partner hangs his body weight on your shoulders, if possible, attempting to force your heels to the ground, resisting for six seconds.

d. Your partner does the same exercise as you resist by hanging your body weight on your shoulders, resisting for six seconds.

e. Each man repeats the exercise three times.

f. When beginning this exercise your partner will not be able to take all of your weight. Begin with only part of your weight and gradually add more weight.

NOTE:

Exercise 5 should also be done on one leg at a time. As your strength increases, add more weight.

Pre-season Conditioning

THE USE OF SALT AND WATER

MANY WRESTLERS and coaches do not realize the extreme importance of taking salt daily and replacing the water that is lost daily. When the salt and water balance in the body is upset, the wrestler suffers in many ways. The physiology is too involved for this book, but briefly this is what happens. Salt helps the body maintain the chemical balance in the body, it slows down the rate of fatigue, and it helps prevent muscle spasm, cramps, muscle injuries, dehydration, heat exhaustion and heat stroke. Water helps regulate the body temperature through sweating. When the body stops sweating, heat exhaustion and heat stroke may result.

When we lose too much salt and water through perspiration, the body fatigues rapidly and the wrestler loses strength, speed, coordination, agility, and all those undefinable qualities of a good wrestler. With extremes in the loss of salt and water, cramping and muscle spasm result. If this continues the wrestler usually receives muscle strains or tears muscle fibers.

I have seen wrestlers dehydrate the body by cutting out water and salt, trying to make weight, that they cramp all over the body. No one knows the long-range effects on the kidneys and other internal organs when you deprive the body of salt and water for extended periods.

When wrestlers dehydrate the body and do not take salt and water, as many wrestlers do when they try to make lower weight classes, many injuries occur.

All wrestlers should take a minimum of six to ten salt pills daily, and the heavier wrestlers should take even more. The light weight high school wrestlers may only need four to six salt pills (5 grain) daily. Consult your team physician for the amount of salt you should be taking for your body weight. Every wrestler should replace the water he loses after every workout. When you sweat off six to ten pounds in a workout you must replace the salt and water for your health's sake.

Salt should be taken throughout the day, not six to ten pills at one time at the end of practice, or whenever you think about it. It is a good idea to take three pillls before practice, three after practice, and three pills before going to bed.

It is also a good idea for the coach to supply the team with enteric-coated salt pills that do not break down quickly. Some wrestlers find that salt pills make them sick. The enteric-coated pills will not make anyone nauseated. It is suggested that these athletes take their salt pills with their meals, and this will usually prevent such sickness. Consult your team physician if you have salt-pill problems.

Take your salt pills and water daily. Anything taken orally takes time until the body breaks it down through digestion and it is in a state that the body can pick it up and use it. The salt you take just before practice cannnot be used by the body for that day's workout. If you forgot to take your salt the day before, you may fatigue, cramp, and have a muscle injury today.

Don't take chances or abuse your body — replace your salt and water daily. Sweating helps the body regulate body temperature — you need plenty of water to prevent heat exhaustion.

SPRINTING

Speed, agility, coordination, and quick moves are essential to all wrestlers. With cardiovascular endurance the wrestler will have all of these qualities.

Sprinting is very necessary for the wrestler. Short sprints with emphasis on quick starts is a better way for the wrestler to get his sprinting.

There are many ways to practice your sprinting. Usually do repeat sprints and time your sprints to measure your progress and improvement in conditioning. Practice your sprints from a track stance and work on starts, sprinting twenty yards. Begin with ten sprints for twenty yards, with ten seconds between each sprint. Mark off twenty yards — start on a whistle and use the stop watch to check your time. Turn around and get back on the starting line for the next sprint. Record the time on each sprint to measure your improvement. As your condition improves your time should be lower and you should be running each sprint in the same time.

Another method of sprinting is to assume the referee's position on the line. On a whistle, jump to your feet and sprint twenty yards. Repeat for ten sprints with ten seconds between each sprint.

All coaches will have their preference as to how far the wrestler should sprint. The best distance is also a matter of opinion, but repeat sprints of short distances of twenty to thirty yards seem to be the best method.

Wrestlers should sprint all year long to maintain their speed and quick starts. There is no better way to keep your weight down than by running. Distance running is fine for all wrestlers in the off-season, and pre-season. A month before the regular season begins the wrestler should do many many short sprints to improve his quick starts and to gain endurance to make quick, explosive starts for nine to twelve minutes. Continue sprinting all during the regular season conditioning program.

DIETS AND CUTTING WEIGHT FOR WRESTLERS

Cutting weight is a controversial subject. If you go about it nutritionally, all wrestling coaches would have fewer problems, both in high school and college.

In high school it would be better to try to wrestle each boy one weight higher from the lightest weight class up to about 137-pound class. You would thus eliminate a big problem high school coaches have with the wrestlers' mothers. Mother is trying to put some weight on her boy and the coach is trying to starve the boy to go down to a lower weight class.

There are a few boys in all weight classes who are a little fat. These boys would do better by losing a little weight. Their body build and fatty tissue will determine if they should lose weight and go down one weight class, and perhaps in a very very few cases, two weight classes. This decision should be left to the school team physician.

It is much better to try to build up the weak, skinny kid who weighs 100 pounds, and go to the next weight class, than to have him lose weight and drop down a weight class.

Weigh all high school wrestling candidates early, at least three months before wrestling practice begins. Use good judgment and try to decide to build up your wrestlers with a good diet and muscle building program rather than by taking every one down one or two weight classes.

With the help of your team physican, set up a good diet for each wrestler, and if the physician thinks it necessary, a diet supplement. There are many good diet supplements on the market today, such as Nutrament, Top Star, and Hustle that are being used by high school, universities, and professional teams in all sports. Many team physicians prescribe vitamins and minerals for some wrestlers. Get a good balanced diet and follow the strength program outlined in the book to build up the strength in each area of the body.

In college the coach has a few different problems. The squad now consists of wrestlers who have perhaps cut too much weight in high school and are now growing rapidly and filling out. Many will never get down to their high school weight class again, even though they were State Champions at a lower weight.

The coach with the help of a team physician should again decide the best weight for each wrestler. Each wrestling candidate should be weighed at least three months before wrestling practice begins. A decision should be made as to which weight class each boy should wrestle in. Have him cut weight gradually if necessary or have him put on more weight so that the day wrestling practice begins he is within three to five pounds of his wrestling weight.

Too many wrestlers, both high school and college, are still fasting, dehydrating the body, and trying to make weight the day of the match, even up to weigh-in time. This breaks all the rules of proper nutrition. The boy loses too much strength and energy working off pounds before weigh-in time the day of the match.

Clinical findings during fasting show wrestlers suffer from (1) early fatigue; (2) decreased endurance; (3) decreased mental alertness; (4) poor speed performance; (5) and poor eye-hand coordination.

Bio-chemical changes during fasting show (1) decreased blood sugar; (2) increased protein utilization; (3) increased water excretion; (4) potassium depletion (essential to proper muscle function); (5) thiamine depletion (vitamin B_1); (6) and increased serum uric acid. The physiology and chemical changes are too technical for this book.

Most wrestlers will lose between two to eight pounds in an average workout depending on their body weight during the regular season. Naturally the heavier weight classes will lose more weight. Nearly all of this daily weight loss is fluid.

Nutritionally, each wrestler needs between 4500 to 6000 calories daily. This too will depend on his body weight. The heavy weight wrestler will probably need the 6000 calories, the light weight, 123 pound wrestler may need 4500 calories.

Food intake depends on what you are trying to do with your body weight. To maintain your present body weight you must burn up most of your daily intake of food. To lose weight you must burn up more calories than you are putting in. To gain weight you must eat more calories than you are burning up and perhaps have a diet supplement (Nutrament, Top Star, or Hustle).

Wrestlers are continually fighting to keep their weight down. They must weigh in and out daily after each workout. On days they do not lose their normal two to five pounds in their workout, they must eat less the next twenty-four hours. When they lose two to five pounds in a workout they may eat their normal amount of food.

For wrestlers to be strong they must have a good, well-balanced diet daily. To have strong wrestlers in each weight class it would be better to have each boy a few pounds under his weight class (wrestle up one weight class), so that he can eat as much as he likes daily and never has to cut weight the week before a match, or in most cases, the day of the match up to weigh-in time. This isn't always possible for many reasons — too many boys in one weight class, too little talent, and injuries in several weight classes.

Here is the best way to handle your weight problems and have good nutrition for the whole wrestling squad. After deciding on a weight class for each boy — he should be at his wrestling weight the first day of practice, and no more than two pounds over his wrestling weight. Let's say the wrestler on the first day of practice weighs in at 132 pounds with his wrestling weight class at 130 pounds. The daily workout should be hard enough for him to lose two to five pounds. He weighed in at 132 pounds and out at 129 pounds after practice.

He can go home and have a well-balanced meal. The next day at the beginning of practice he will weigh in again at 132 or perhaps at 130 pounds. This way the wrestler never has to fast or dehydrate the body to make weight for a match. By watching his weight and food intake daily, his wrestling weight remains about the same. He is always strong and ready to wrestle if he keeps his weight down.

On the days he does not lose two to five pounds in a workout, he will not be able to eat as much this night after practice.

Nutritionally for all sports, diets should be regulated in the following way. Forty-eight hours before every contest the athlete should eat a diet high in carbohydrate food to store energy building foods. Twenty-four hours before the contest or wrestling match the wrestler should rest.

Most wrestlers do not do this. They are starving and dehydrating a week before a wrestling match and most are working out and dehydrating right up to weigh-in time. This is why we have many wrestling injuries and many weak wrestlers.

Weigh in before practice and weigh out after practice. Your weight loss for the day will determine how much you may eat at your evening meal. Watch your weight closely and eat a balanced diet every day. For strength it is better to wrestle up one weight class so you can eat all you want and drink all the fluid you want every day. This isn't always possible on every team, but each wrestler should weigh in daily before practice at his wrestling weight, or a little under.

Cutting weight correctly is the biggest problem for the wrestler and wrestling coach. Try to cut weight as suggested, and you'll have fewer problems cutting weight.

Regular Seasonal Conditioning

WHEN FALL practice begins in high school and in college, most of the coaches do not spend as much time on conditioning. Wrestlers are expected to report at their wrestling weight in good physical condition — both cardiovascular and strengthwise.

Practice will be devoted to teaching fundamentals, to drills to practice the fundamentals, to learning new moves and holds — both offensively and defensively.

Should you be overweight and out of condition, the coaches do not have time to waste trying to get you in shape. Usually you'll be injured before the first week of practice is finished, trying to keep up with the team or trying to protect a weak knee, shoulder, or back. You are cheating the team and yourself if you do not report the first day of regular practice ready to wrestle at the previously assigned wrestling weight class. Many coaches will not let you come out for practice if you are overweight. This is a good idea and saves a lot of valuable practice time.

If coaches want strong wrestlers they must add strength work to their daily program. Wrestlers will do only as much as the coach requires them to do. After ten minutes of vigorous warm-up and stretching exercise, you should have ten to twenty minutes of strength exercises. If you have a limited budget, as do most high schools and many colleges, you can use the two-man isometric exercise program described on pages 60-83.

Follow the program listed below at least once a day after the warm-up exercises until two days before each wrestling match. Do three six-second contractions of each exercise. Exercise at different positions through a complete range of motion. Follow the exercise directions closely to be sure the exercises are done correctly. You do not have to push so hard that you see sparks or think you will black out. You can gain strength pushing 60 to 80 percent of your best effort. Always push short of the point of pain. If you get pain during any exercise you will only keep the muscle sore. Exercise without pain.

1. Neck exercise (in all four directions). 60
2. Shoulder exercise.
   Shoulder flexion. 61
   Shoulder abduction. 61
   Shoulder horizontal extension. 61
   Shoulder elevation sideward. 63
3. Chest exercise. 69-70   28,29,10,91,32
4. Abdominal exercise.
   Bent knee sit-up. 71
5. Back exercise. 72-74
   Thigh extension (straight leg raising). 73 74
   Thigh extension (straight leg raising higher range.)
6. Knee exercise (use the bleachers, or put tables in the wrestling area).
   Knee extension (90 degrees).
   Knee extension (135 degrees).
   Knee extension (165 degrees).
   Knee flexion (165 degrees) lying on the wrestling mats.
   Knee flexion (135 degrees) lying on the wrestling mats.
7. Ankle exercise.
   Ankle inversion.
   Ankle dorsi-flexion.
   Ankle eversion
   Plantar flexion (rise on toes — legs straight).
   Plantar flexion (rise on toes — knees bent to 135 degrees).

Check the index for the page numbers of the exercise program listed above.

All of these areas must be strong in order to wrestle. If time is a factor, you can work fifteen minutes a day. One day you work the neck, shoulders, chest and abdominals, and the next day you can work the back, knee, and ankle exercises — three days a week on the upper body and three days a week on the lower body. Wrestlers with old injuries and weak joints will work daily to strengthen the weak area after practice.

If budgets permit, you should have a half-dozen chinning bars and parallel bars near the wrestling room or area for daily thirty-six-second pull-ups and shoulder dips. Everyone will do three thirty-six-second pull-ups and shoulder dips daily and three thirty-six-second push-ups before and after practice. As these become easy, resistance may be added by wearing a weighted vest or by holding a weight between the knees while doing your pull-up or shoulder dip. The coaches will supervise and count for everyone. These should be done five days a week up to the day before a wrestling match. Twenty-four hours before the wrestling match the wrestler should do nothing but rest.

Devote fifteen to twenty minutes of each day to strength isometric exercise, and you will have a much stronger team and very few injuries. Each wrestler should continually do isometric exercise daily on his own to strengthen his weak area, and to restrengthen every sprain, or contusion until they are back to normal strength.

Should the coach or trainer think the wrestlers are weak in any other area, other isometric exercises should be added to the program and the isometric exercises omitted where the wrestlers are strong.

Many college and high school teams are now using The Spackman Isometric Leg Exerciser.* This unit was developed and researched at Southern Illinois University, Carbondale, Illinois, and is used in the training and wrestling area.

On The Spackman Leg Exerciser, you can work all the muscles in the ankle, knee, hip, back, abdomen, and neck. A complete exercise manual goes with each unit. The exercise unit sells for $160.00. See the pictures below.

---

*Manufactured by La Berne Manufacturing Co., 819 Leesburg Road, Columbia, S.C. 29205.

Ankle Inversion

Knee Extension at 90°

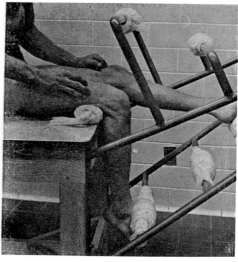

Knee Extension at 165°

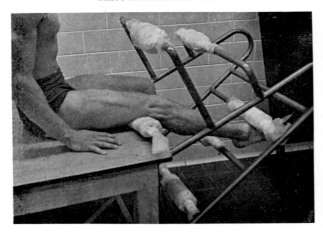

Hip Flexion

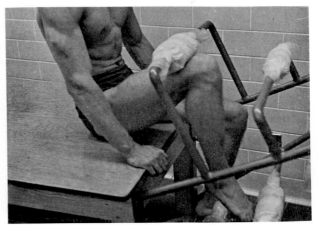

Knee Flexion at 135°

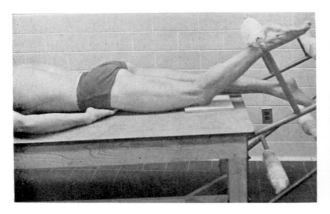

Hip Extension

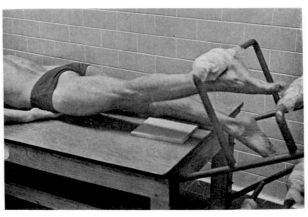

Neck Extension

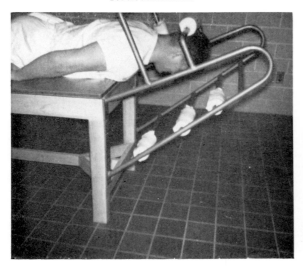

Lateral Neck Flexion

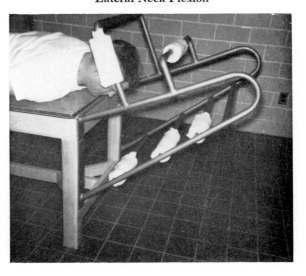

Leg exercisers are mounted on each end of eight-foot tables. Coaches have several eight-foot tables with leg-exercisers on each end of the table. With several tables by the wrestling area or wrestling room.

Wrestling is a strong man's sport, so if a coach wants strong athletes, he has to put strength exercise in the daily practice program. He shows them what he wants to do and then counts for them. Boys with injuries will work daily in the training room on the leg exerciser under the trainer's or coach's supervision.

Neck Flexion

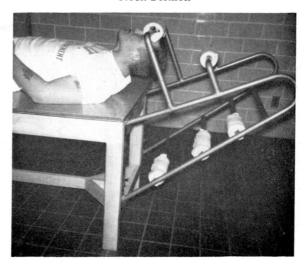

BEFORE EVERY WRESTLING MATCH

Most wrestlers have an informal warm-up and stretching program before the match. Many just stretch and roll around on the mats with a teammate practicing a few moves. Others will skip rope or run in place. Warming up is an individual problem. Do what you think best to get yourself ready for your match. Give yourself enough time to get loose and break a sweat before your match. The older college wrestler will usually need more stretching and time to warm up than the younger high school wrestler. Be sure you are stretched out, loose, warm, and have broken a good sweat before your match begins.

Conclusion

Conditioning for wrestling is a difficult task. There is a constant battle to keep your strength at a high level and your weight on or very close to your wrestling weight class. Wrestling is a tough, grueling sport for the boy who loves body contact.

Workouts are hard and long, and it takes a boy with tremendous willpower to be a good wrestler. Like most boys they are hungry all the time, and wrestling season comes at a time when everyone is eating large meals at Thanksgiving, Christmas, and New Year holidays. Usually the wrestler cannot eat too much and still maintain his wrestling weight. This is a very difficult time for the wrestler.

Once the first day of practice begins there has never been a wrestler who is 100 percent. He has a daily new contusion, strain, sprain, and abrasion. He must work constantly to gain and maintain his muscle strength and get treatments to heal his new injury.

He must diet and watch his weight daily to maintain his present weight. He must weigh in daily at his wrestling weight class and work hard in practice to lose a few pounds, so he can eat tonight and tomorrow. He is constantly fighting the battle of the bulge.

In the off-season he must work on strength to rebuild his old or new injuries and constantly try to increase his overall body strength.

In the pre-season he has to begin again to cut weight to get back to his weight class, or wrestle in a heavier weight class. Through normal growth and maturity the wrestler will have to wrestle at a heavier weight class. Too many wrestlers continue to try to wrestle at the same weight class for four years in high school, and for four more years in college. This cutting weight may be injurious to the boy's health.

Wrestlers should be put on a supervised, prescribed exercise program for their individual needs. Coaches should consult their team physician and trainer for a program for each wrestler. Have the physician decide the correct weight class for each wrestler according to his body structure and present physical condition.

When wrestling season ends, you may rest a week or two. Then begin playing handball, tennis, swimming, or basketball, or participate in some other active sport to maintain your speed, flexibility and cardiovascular endurance. Play some vigorous sport at least three days a week for an hour to an hour and a half. Do isometric exercise, lift weights, do pull-ups, push-ups, and shoulder dips to maintain or improve your strength. Work out hard in the off-season and you can eat almost anything you want. Never allow yourself to gain too much weight or get fat. Try to stay close to your wrestling weight class unless you are growing and maturing and plan to wrestle in a heavier weight class. Weigh yourself daily and never let yourself get fat. It's too hard to get the weight off in your pre-season conditioning program.

All wrestlers must have tremendous strength, flexibility, agility, balance, speed, and endurance. Work constantly to get the whole body stronger. More strength will give you better balance, agility, speed, and endurance. Stay strong and work out twelve months a year, and you will have a long, injury-free wrestling career.

Index